UNWIND YOUR BRAIN

The Ultimate Guide to Stop Overthinking, Manage Stress and Master Your Emotions

Simone Keys

Index

Introduction

I'm sitting in my favorite coffee shop, watching the hustle and bustle of the people around me, and I realize that stress is inevitable. We can't escape it, and there seems to be no way around it these days. We all experience stress at some point in our lives, whether it's the demands of work, family responsibilities, financial or health problems.

The subject of stress has always intrigued me. Perhaps it is because I have had several experiences that have triggered it. I know firsthand how damaging it can be, as I have experienced it at all stages of my life. From my days as a college student, preparing for exams, to the present day, when I am trying to accomplish multiple different tasks at the same time.

But what does the term "stress" really mean and why does it have such a significant impact on our lives? As I delved deeper into the subject, I discovered that stress is a physiological response our bodies experience to imagined situations of trouble or danger.

When our brain perceives a stressful situation, chemicals such as cortisol and adrenaline are released, preparing the body for the "fight or flight" response.

This response can be useful in some circumstances, such as when we need to escape from real danger, but it can become detrimental if it becomes a constant regulation. Chronic stress has even been linked to physical and mental health problems, such as hypertension, heart disease and depression.

As I delved deeper into my studies of stress, I became aware of its complexity and multifaceted nature. Our environment, the people we interact with and even our own thought patterns can influence how we feel emotionally and mentally at any given moment.

However, the more I learned about the subject, the more I became interested in discovering how we can manage stress without resorting to unhealthy behaviors, such as binge eating or drug use, so over the years, I tried many different methods of coping with stress, such as meditation, exercise and psychotherapy, among others.

Through experience, I discovered that there are key strategies that help us cope with stress more constructively. Some have been more successful than others, but I have learned a lot in the process of exploring all of these options.

I know this book will become an invaluable resource in your quest to learn and apply these strategies in your daily life. Through the tips and techniques I will share with you, you will find effective ways to manage stress, whether it is caused by work, family, or everyday pressures.

I confess that I have no medical training, nor am I a professional therapist, but I want to share my perspective with you and the lessons I have learned from my own experiences. I am convinced that this point of view can be useful and valuable, especially for those who are struggling with the challenge of stress.

I look forward to helping you regain calm and balance in your life. Whether you are a busy professional trying to balance work and family, a student overwhelmed by exams and homework, or simply someone who feels that stress is taking over your life, I am here to accompany you on this journey of self-discovery and personal growth.

Ultimately, I firmly believe that together we can contribute to making the world a better and healthier place. Starting with our own lives, we will be better prepared to face life's challenges and build stronger, more resilient communities and societies by learning to manage stress effectively.

I welcome you to this journey to a calmer, more balanced, stress-free life.

CHAPTER 1

Stress: its impact on your well-being

Definition of stress and its influence on physical and mental health

Stress is a natural, physiological response that we experience when faced with situations that we perceive as challenging, threatening or demanding. It is a reaction of the organism that activates different systems, such as the nervous and endocrine systems, and can manifest itself both physically and emotionally.

Stress can be triggered by a variety of factors, such as work, studies, personal relationships or major life changes. While some levels of stress can be normal and motivating, chronic or excessive stress can have negative effects on our health and well-being. It is important to learn to manage it properly in order to maintain balance and well-being in our daily lives.

Did you know that it can trigger hormonal fluctuations that impact our physical health? From speeding up our heart rate to weakening our immune system and making us more susceptible to disease, stress can wreak havoc.

But that is not all. We must also take into account the psychological effects that can be disabling.

Persistent anxiety, depression and irritability can make even the most basic tasks of daily life difficult, reducing our mental capacity and our ability to remember information. In addition, stress can disrupt our rest, leaving us exhausted and unprepared to face daily challenges.

However, I want to convey a message of hope. By reflecting on how stress is disconnected from our lives, we can use that knowledge to take action in the future. We can take a focused approach to our emotional and mental well-being. If you are feeling the negative effects of stress, let me tell you that you are not alone. Many of us experience these challenges, but we must not lose hope.

Through self-care and stress reduction, we can discover peace and harmony. By implementing appropriate tactics and exercises, we can lessen its impact on our lives and find a greater sense of calm and enjoyment in the present.

Recognizing the signs of stress in your body

As someone who has experienced the ravages of chronic stress, I know how difficult it is to detect the early signs that our bodies are on the verge of collapse. Stress can be so insidious that it can weaken us, both physically and mentally, without us realizing what is happening. We can become helpless and isolated. That's why it's crucial to watch for early signs and address them before they spiral out of control and leave us breathless.

Since stress can surprise us and manifest itself in a variety of ways, it is important to pay attention to these warning signs. We may experience stabbing pain that starts in the neck and spreads to the shoulders and back. We may also suffer from severe headaches or feel exhausted and drained, even after getting enough sleep.

On a mental level, signs of stress include anxiety disorders, panic attacks and racing thoughts, which can make us feel helpless and on the verge of a nervous breakdown. Depressive symptoms are also common, and we may feel hopeless, have difficulty concentrating, forget things and become irritable even with the people who love us most.

However, there are techniques and physical activities that can help us better manage stress and regain control of our lives. Exercise releases endorphins that improve our mood, while deep breathing helps us relax both mind and body.

The practice of mindfulness meditation allows us to tune into our inner world, and yoga is a wonderful way to calm our nerves and improve our health. Both methods increase our awareness of inner experience. In addition, seeking emotional support from friends and family in difficult times makes us feel that we are not alone.

The first step in creating effective strategies for dealing with stress is to recognize the physical manifestations of stress in our bodies. With effort, patience and taking responsibility for our lives, we can learn to cope with stress and enjoy the present moment.

Let's embark on this adventure together and emerge victorious in our fight against stress!

Practical exercises for stress management

When the demands of everyday life don't let up, it may seem like fighting stress is an uphill battle. Fear not, however, because there are actions you can take to calm your mind, improve your health and find overall happiness.

Let me share with you some exercises that I have personally found effective in relieving stress and elevating my mood.

A wonderful technique for relieving stress and cultivating a more positive attitude toward life is to keep a "gratitude journal". Spend a few minutes each day writing down three things you are grateful for, no matter how small they may seem.

If you enjoy creative activities such as painting, drawing or writing, these can be effective ways to manage stress. By focusing on the moment and positively releasing negative emotions, you can achieve two goals at once.

Physical activity is essential. If you want to feel better and have less stress in your life, it's crucial that you set aside time to exercise regularly. Find something you really enjoy, such as walking, running or yoga, and incorporate it into your routine.

Last but not least, social interaction has been shown to relieve stress and improve mood. Spend more time with friends and family, organize dinner outings or watch a movie together. Seek the company of optimistic and encouraging people, as they will help you feel better about yourself.

Depending on your schedule and personal goals, you can implement any of these steps, alone or in combination. The most important thing is that you choose a method that works for you and follow it consistently. You can learn to cope with stress and enjoy life in the here and now, it just takes a little time and effort.

In the next sections of this book, we will delve into specific exercises and methods to regulate your feelings and thoughts. You will learn to control your stress and lead a more positive and healthy life without letting stress control you.

Remember that you are capable of doing it!

Identifying sources of stress in your life

Let me be your guide in this journey towards identifying the sources of stress in your life. Today I invite you to reflect on the various situations and elements that may be generating stress in your daily life. Through this exploration, you will discover valuable tools to free yourself from their negative influence and live a more balanced and fulfilling life. As we all know, modern life can be fast-paced and demanding. Work responsibilities, personal relationships, financial worries and daily challenges can pile up, all of which can overwhelm us and rob us of our peace of mind.

That's why it's crucial that you take a moment to analyze what specific factors are contributing to your stress. Here are some common areas to consider:

Work: We spend a large part of our lives in the work environment. Does your current job provide you with satisfaction and a sense of purpose, or are you stuck in a routine that drains you emotionally and physically? Reflect on whether your work is in harmony with your values and whether it gives you the opportunity to grow and develop professionally.

Personal relationships: interactions with others can be a source of both joy and stress. Look at your close relationships: do you feel supported and loved, or do you experience tension and conflict? Be sure to set healthy boundaries and surround yourself with people who give you positive energy and push you to be the best version of yourself.

Finances: Financial worries can generate a great deal of stress in our lives. Evaluate your relationship with money and analyze if your spending and saving habits are aligned with your long-term goals. Establishing a realistic budget and developing an abundance mindset will allow you to take control of your finances and reduce the associated stress.

Self-care: Many times, we neglect our own health and well-being in the midst of daily demands. Do you take enough time to rest, relax and nourish your body and mind? Remember that taking care of yourself is a priority, not a luxury. Practice activities that bring you calm and satisfaction, such as meditating, exercising, reading or spending time outdoors.

Unreasonable expectations: Often, we put undue pressure on ourselves by trying to meet unrealistic expectations, both self-imposed and societal. Reflect on whether you are trying to be perfect in all areas of your life and whether this creates necessary stress. Learn to accept yourself as you are and set achievable goals that allow you to grow without overwhelming yourself.

Remember that identifying sources of stress is the first step toward change. Once you recognize the elements that broke you down negatively, you can take concrete steps to minimize their impact on your life.

Don't be afraid to seek professional help if necessary. Therapists, counselors or counselors can provide you with additional tools to manage stress effectively.

I encourage you to take some time to reflect on the different sources of stress in your life. Remember that you are the protagonist of your own story and you have the power to transform it. Don't let stress rob you of joy and inner peace. Trust yourself and take the necessary steps to live a more balanced, fulfilled and serene life.

CHAPTER 2

Mindfulness: cultivating wholeness in each moment

Discovering the magic of mindfulness: The transformative power of the here and now.

Mindfulness, also known as mindfulness, invites us to immerse ourselves in the present moment with full awareness and acceptance. It is an art that allows us to awaken and savor each experience of life with an open mind and compassionate heart. By practicing mindfulness, we can free ourselves from the chains of stress and find the inner peace we long for.

This ancient practice provides us with a series of profound benefits to reduce stress and improve our overall well-being. By being fully present in the here and now, we free ourselves from the worries of the past and the anxieties of the future, allowing us to fully enjoy each moment. Mindfulness helps us to calm the mind, reduce anxiety and cultivate greater mental and emotional clarity.

By practicing mindfulness on a regular basis, we can train our minds to be aware of our thoughts, emotions and bodily sensations without judging them or reacting impulsively. This allows us to respond in a more balanced and compassionate way to life's challenges, rather than falling into automatic patterns of stress and reactivity.

Immersing ourselves in practice: Tips and exercises to cultivate mindfulness

Mindfulness is a practice that can be easily incorporated into our daily lives, giving us the opportunity to experience wholeness in every moment. Here are some mindfulness practices that you can integrate into your daily routine:

a) Mindfulness of breathing: take a few minutes a day to focus on your breathing. Observe how the air enters and leaves your body, feeling each inhalation and exhalation. If your mind wanders, you can gently redirect it to the sensation of the breath. This exercise helps you to calm the mind and be present in the present moment.

b) Mindfulness in daily activities: perform a common activity, such as washing the dishes, with full attention. Feel the warm water in your hands, notice the colors and textures of the dishes, and appreciate each mindful movement. In doing so, you transform an ordinary task into an opportunity to connect with yourself and the world around you.

c) Mindfulness in walking: when you walk, focus on each step you take. Feel the contact of your feet with the ground, the sensation of your muscles moving and the breeze caressing your skin. Notice the details of your environment and connect with the beauty of nature around you. Mindful walking helps you to anchor yourself in the present and find calm in movement.

Beginning your mindfulness meditation journey: find tranquility in daily practice.

Mindfulness meditation is a powerful tool for cultivating greater mental clarity and inner serenity. Begin your meditation practice by finding a quiet, comfortable place where you can sit in a relaxed but alert posture.

Begin by focusing your attention on your breath, feeling the air moving in and out of your body. As your mind wanders to other thoughts, simply observe them without judgment and gently redirect your attention to the breath. Allow your thoughts to flow and leave without attaching yourself to them.

You can start with short meditation sessions of five to ten minutes a day and gradually build up. As you progress, you can explore different meditation approaches, such as body scanning, guided meditation or loving-kindness meditation.

Remember that mindfulness practice is an ongoing and personal process. Don't push yourself too hard and be kind to yourself along the way. With consistent practice, you will begin to experience the transformative benefits of mindfulness in your daily life.

Benefits of mindfulness for health and wellbeing

Mindfulness can be one of our greatest allies if we want to reduce stress and improve our health and well-being, among other reasons the practice of *mindfulness* allows us:

Reducing stress and anxiety: finding balance in daily life. Mindfulness offers a powerful tool for reducing the stress and anxiety we face in our daily lives. By practicing mindfulness, we learn to be present in the present moment and cultivate a healthy relationship with our emotions and thoughts. This allows us to find balance in daily life, freeing us from the burden of stress and excessive anxiety.

Improve concentration and productivity: by focusing and having greater efficiency in Tasks. Our ability to concentrate is strengthened when we are present in the present moment. The practice of mindfulness teaches us to focus our attention on one task at a time, preventing mental dispersion. This leads to a significant improvement in our ability to concentrate on our tasks and increase our productivity efficiently.

Mental and emotional well-being: Mindfulness provides us with the tools to cultivate a lasting state of mental and emotional well-being. By being present in each moment, we develop greater emotional stability and a greater ability to manage stress. It also fosters resilience, allowing us to recover more quickly from life's challenges and difficulties.

Integrating mindfulness into interpersonal relationships

Mindfulness helps us improve our communication skills by fostering mindful listening and deep understanding. By being fully present in a conversation, we can cultivate empathy and understanding for others, creating an environment of respect and genuine connection.

Similarly, the practice of mindfulness allows us to develop and maintain healthy and meaningful interpersonal relationships. By being present in our interactions, we can connect on a deeper level with others, fostering empathy and mutual support. This contributes to more satisfying and enriching relationships.

Mindfulness also helps us to address conflicts in a mindful and peaceful manner. We can respond rather than react impulsively by being present in the present moment during challenges. This allows us to find creative solutions and transform conflicts into opportunities for personal growth and to relate well with others.

24

Integrating mindfulness into the professional and working world

Mindfulness has a significant impact on our work world when we improve our focus and clarity at work. By being fully present in our work tasks, we can perform them with greater efficiency and accuracy, which in turn generates an increase in our productivity and performance.

On the other hand, the practice of mindfulness helps us to find a healthy balance between our personal and professional lives. We can establish clear boundaries and appropriate requirements by being present in every aspect of our lives. This will allow us to enjoy greater harmony and satisfaction in all areas of our lives.

The practice of mindfulness also has a powerful impact on leadership. Mindful leaders practice mindfulness in the way they communicate, make decisions and manage their team. By being mindful and authentic, they inspire people to reach their full potential and create a positive work environment and other motivators.

Obstacles and opportunities for mindfulness practice.

When we begin the practice of mindfulness, we may encounter some obstacles, but don't lose heart, everything has a solution. The wandering mind is a common obstacle to mindfulness practice. However, through persistence and patience, we can cultivate a greater ability to redirect our attention to the present moment.

It is also important to remind ourselves to be kind and compassionate to ourselves when the mind is distracted, thus encouraging self-compassion in our mindfulness journey.

Incorporating mindfulness into our daily routine helps us remember that every moment can be an opportunity to practice mindful presence. Whether it is eating, walking or performing daily tasks, we can transform these moments into meaningful experiences by being very present and connected to ourselves and our surroundings.

Maintaining a long-term mindfulness practice requires motivation and constant reminders. Setting visual reminders, practicing in groups, and finding sources of inspiration are effective ways to keep our practice active.

It is also useful to remember the benefits we experience through mindfulness, which motivates us to continue and deepen our path of personal growth.

CHAPTER 3

Detachment: Embracing the Release of Negative Thoughts and Emotions

The magic of letting go: transforming the impact of negative thoughts and emotions

In this chapter on liberation, we will explore the transformative power of letting go of the negative thoughts and emotions that limit us. Understanding the impact these energies have on our lives is the first step to finding the emotional and mental freedom we crave.

When we hold on to negative thoughts and emotions, we allow them to pollute our minds and rob us of joy and inner peace. It's like carrying a heavy backpack full of worries, resentments and constant self-criticism. But we don't have to carry that unnecessary weight.

By becoming aware of how negative thoughts influence our perceptions and actions, we open the door to profound change. We realize that we have the power to free ourselves from these attachments and create a more positive and fulfilling life.

Tools to embrace emotional and mental freedom

Now is the time to delve into the techniques that help us to free ourselves from emotional and mental negativity.

Here are some practical tools that you can apply in your daily life:

a) Thought transformation: observe your negative thoughts without judging them. Recognize that you are not your thoughts and that you have the power to change them. Replace negative thoughts with positive, constructive affirmations. For example, if you find yourself thinking, "I am not good enough," change it to "I am valuable and capable of achieving whatever I set my mind to."

b) The dance of emotions: allow yourself to feel your negative emotions without resistance. Recognize that emotions are temporary and do not define you as a person. Accept that it is natural to experience a wide range of emotions and find healthy ways to process them, such as talking to a loved one or writing in a journal.

c) Transformative gratitude: cultivate gratitude as a daily practice. Focus on the positive things in your life and express your gratitude. Keep a gratitude journal where you write down three things you are grateful for each day. This will help you shift your focus to the positive and attract more joy into your life.

Exercises to embrace liberation

Now, I invite you to immerse yourself in concrete exercises that will help you let go of negativity and embrace liberation:

a) The ritual of letting go: write on a piece of paper all the negative thoughts and emotions you wish to release. Then, burn the paper safely, visualizing how these energies transform into ashes and dissolve into the air. Feel the lightness and space that is created within you.

b) The visualization of renewal: close your eyes and visualize a beautiful and peaceful landscape. Imagine that you are letting go of all emotional and mental burdens. With each breath, feel how you are filled with light and peace. Imagine how this new state allows you to move freely and open yourself to new positive experiences.

c) Practicing self-care: Take time each day to take care of yourself. Engage in activities that bring you joy and relaxation, such as taking a relaxing bath, reading an inspirational book, or taking a walk in nature. Remember that taking care of yourself is an act of love and a powerful way to move away from negativity.

You will discover a renewed sense of freedom and lightness by practicing these exercises and tools. You will open yourself to a world full of possibilities and live a fuller, more authentic life.

The importance of self-care in the detachment process

Self-care is a fundamental pillar in our journey toward freedom from negative thoughts and emotions. Focusing on self-care provides a comforting refuge and inspires us to reach new heights.

Our body is a sacred temple that deserves to be lovingly cared for. We do this by eating consciously, choosing nutritious foods that give us energy and vitality, or by taking time to listen to our body's needs and providing it with the rest and restorative sleep it requires. Each step we take toward healthy eating and proper rest brings us closer to our inner harmony.

The mind of each of us is like a garden, and we must nurture it with positive and loving thoughts. Let's practice mindfulness to recognize and release negative thought patterns. Allow yourself moments of tranquility and peace of mind through meditation, mindful breathing or any other practice that makes you feel in harmony with yourself. Focusing on your mental well-being will help you detach from negative emotions and cultivate a clear and serene mind.

Connecting with nature is an inexhaustible source of inspiration and healing. Allow yourself to enjoy the beauty that surrounds us: a sunrise painting the sky, birdsong or a walk in the woods. Take time to connect with the earth, feeling the breeze on your skin and the earth beneath your feet. Nature teaches us to let go and flow, reminding us that we are part of a larger whole.

Another way to take care of ourselves is by learning to say "no": Detachment also involves freeing ourselves from necessary burdens and learning to set healthy boundaries. Don't be afraid to say "no" when something is not aligned with your needs or values. Recognize that your time and energy are valuable and deserve to be spent on what really matters. By setting boundaries, you empower yourself and open yourself up to new opportunities for growth and well-being.

Celebrate self-care in community, remembering that you are not alone in this journey. Seek the support and companionship of those who share your values and encourage you to take care of yourself. Together, we can create a space of love and understanding where self-care is celebrated and encouraged. Through collaboration and mutual support, we strengthen and remind ourselves of the importance of taking care of ourselves.

Self-care is a gift you can give yourself at every stage of your life. By nourishing your body, calming your mind and setting healthy boundaries, it opens you up to a deeper and more transformative experience of detachment.

Allow yourself to receive the love and attention you deserve and remember that self-care is an act of love for yourself and others. Together, we can embrace liberation and live a full and meaningful life.

Living in the present: freeing ourselves from the past and worrying about the future

Focusing on the present allows us to free ourselves from the weight of the past and the anxiety of the future. Let me share with you the beauty of living fully in the here and now, where life really happens. I invite you to explore the following key points to embrace this liberation:

Let go of the past: the past no longer defines us. Let us accept that we cannot change what has happened, but we can choose how we relate to it. Let us acknowledge the lessons we have learned and forgive ourselves and others for any past pain or mistakes. By letting go of the burdens of the past, we create space to experience joy and fulfillment in the present.

Cultivate gratitude for the present moment: the present is a gift. Take a moment to appreciate the little things in life: the gentle breeze caressing your face, the warm embrace of a loved one, the aroma of coffee in the morning. Practice gratitude, recognizing the blessings that surround you at this moment. In doing so, you find yourself in a state of openness and joy, attracting more positive things into your life.

Focus attention on the here and now: the mind tends to wander between the past and the future, but the power lies in the present. Cultivate mindfulness by directing your focus to the present moment. Observe your thoughts and emotions without judgment, simply allowing them to be and then letting them go. By being fully present, we connect with the essence of life and free ourselves from worry and anxiety.

Practice conscious breathing: Breathing is an anchor to the present. Take a moment to focus on your breath, feeling the air moving in and out of your body. Notice how you connect with the natural rhythm of life. Conscious breathing helps us to be present, to find calm in the midst of chaos and to rediscover inner peace.

Embrace the uncertainty of the future: worrying about the future only robs us of the joy of the present. Accept that the future is unknown and embrace the uncertainty with confidence. Instead of worrying about what's next, focus on what you can do today to build the future you want. Trust in your ability to meet any challenge that comes your way and live each day with determination and gratitude.

By living fully in the present, we free ourselves from the burdens of the past and from anxiety about the future. Let us seize this moment, for it is in this instant that we find true happiness and inner peace. We deserve to live a life full of love, joy and fulfillment.

CHAPTER 4

Gratitude: awakening the power of positive thinking

Opening our hearts to gratitude: Its power in mental health

Gratitude is much more than just a word; it is a practice that connects us to the beauty and abundance of every moment of our lives.

When we open our hearts to gratitude, we create space for the positive and nurture our minds with love and appreciation. Gratitude allows us to focus on the blessings around us, even in difficult times, and helps us see the light in the darkness.

Cultivating a garden of gratitude in daily life

Gratitude is a powerful habit that we can cultivate in our daily lives. Here are some practical ways to integrate gratitude into your routine:

a) The gratitude journal: set aside a few minutes each day to write the things you are grateful for in a journal. They can be big or small blessings, such as a kind smile from a stranger, a warm cup of tea or a peaceful moment in nature. By focusing on the positive, you will cultivate an attitude of gratitude that will expand into all areas of your life.

b) The power of words: express your gratitude to the people around you. Take the time to say "thank you" in a genuine and sincere way. Acknowledge their kind words and actions. In doing so, you will not only cultivate gratitude in yourself, but you will also sow seeds of love and appreciation in the hearts of others.

c) The visualization of gratitude: before going to sleep, close your eyes and visualize all the moments of gratitude you experienced during the day. Relive those feelings and allow them to flood you with happiness and peace. As you bring this practice into your life, you will begin to notice more things to be grateful for, creating a virtuous cycle of positivity and abundance.

Exercises for practicing gratitude in every moment

Now, I invite you to participate in practical exercises that will help you integrate gratitude into every moment of your life:

a) The gratitude breath: take a few moments to breathe deeply. As you inhale, think of something you are grateful for at that moment. As you exhale, release any tension or worry. Feel gratitude flood your whole being and fill you with peace.

b) Focus on the positive: Consciously observe the positive things around you throughout the day. It could be the sun shining in the sky, the scent of flowers or an inspiring conversation. By focusing on the positive, you train your mind to see the beauty and abundance in every moment.

c) The act of service: look for opportunities to help others in a selfless way. By giving your time, skills or support to those in need, you will experience gratitude in action. At the same time, you will be creating a positive impact on the lives of others, showing a chain of kindness and gratitude.

Gratitude is a choice we can make in every moment. By embracing it, we transform our perspective and allow happiness and love to flood our lives.

Gratitude as a transformer of interpersonal relationships

In our journey towards inner serenity, balance and tranquility, the awakening of gratitude must be present, as its influence extends beyond our mental health and our daily lives. Gratitude has the power to transform our interpersonal relationships, enriching our connections and strengthening our emotional bonds.

The magic of gratitude can strengthen family bonds and create an atmosphere of unconditional love and support. Recognizing the blessings that each member of our family brings to our lives and how to express gratitude in a sincere and regular manner will always be helpful, as this simple act can uplift the family spirit and foster a sense of unity and harmony.

As we expand our network of gratitude to our friends and loved ones, we will understand how gratitude can deepen our friendships and close relationships. I invite you to reflect on the people around you and the ways in which they have positively impacted your life and to express gratitude in an authentic way, so you will see how your bonds with them are strengthened and how a virtuous circle of support and love is created.

Gratitude not only benefits our existing relationships, but can also open us to new connections and friendships. Cultivating an attitude of gratitude can cause us to approach others with an open and generous heart, allowing us to recognize and appreciate the unique qualities of the people we meet, creating a solid foundation for building meaningful and lasting relationships.

Expressing gratitude in the workplace can strengthen our professional lives and contribute to a positive and productive work environment. Recognizing and appreciating the contributions of our colleagues, superiors and subordinates promotes a sense of camaraderie, increases motivation and improves overall well-being in the work environment.

Gratitude is a powerful tool that allows us to enrich our interpersonal relationships. As we practice gratitude toward our families, friends, loved ones and colleagues, we nurture our connections, create a sense of belonging and promote a more loving and compassionate world.

Continue your journey of gratitude, and you will see how this wonderful practice transforms not only your personal life, but also the way you relate to others.

Let me remind you that the power of gratitude resides in your heart, and every day is an opportunity to open it and share its light with those around you.

CHAPTER 5

The art of happiness: discovering joy in each day

Cultivating satisfaction and psychological well-being

Happiness is not just a destination, but a journey we can consciously embark on to live a full and satisfying life. Scientific studies have shown that there is a close relationship between contentment and psychological well-being. When we learn to nurture our minds and heart, we can experience a significant increase in our overall happiness and well-being.

On our path to joy and inner serenity, it is essential to dedicate time and effort to cultivate our satisfaction and psychological well-being, that is why I want to share with you some reflections and practices that can help you in this wonderful process of self-discovery and self-transformation.

Recognize your personal worth: Start by acknowledging that you are a valuable person and deserving of love and happiness. Don't let self-criticism or comparison with others discourage you. Love yourself and value your qualities and accomplishments, no matter how small. Remember that you are unique and special.

Practice self-compassion: Often, we are harder on ourselves than we would be on our loved ones. Learn to treat yourself with kindness and gentleness. Allow yourself to make mistakes and learn from them. Cultivate patience and tolerance with yourself. Recognize that you deserve care and understanding at all times.

Find your purpose: Connecting with a meaningful purpose in life can generate deep satisfaction and psychological well-being. Reflect on what you are passionate about and what fills you with joy. Ask yourself what contribution you want to make to the world and how you can use your talents and skills to achieve it. Set goals aligned with your purpose and take steady steps toward their realization.

Practice gratitude: Gratitude is a powerful antidote to dissatisfaction and discomfort. Each day, take a moment to appreciate the blessings and positive things you have in your life. Keep a gratitude journal where you record at least three things you are grateful for. This practice will help you focus on the good and cultivate a positive attitude.

Take care of your emotional well-being: Emotional self-care is essential to maintaining psychological well-being and satisfaction. Spend time in activities that bring you joy and inner peace. Seek moments of tranquility and relaxation, whether through meditation, mindfulness practice or creative activities that you enjoy. Prioritize adequate rest and sleep, and seek the support of people you trust when you need it.

Cultivate healthy relationships: Our relationships with others play a crucial role in our psychological well-being. Seek authentic and meaningful connections with people who support you, inspire you and make you feel valued. Practice empathy and active listening in your interactions, and cultivate relationships based on mutual respect and reciprocity.

Remember that the path to fulfillment and psychological well-being is unique to each of us. Allow yourself to explore and discover the practices and approaches that resonate with you. Cultivate your inner self with love, compassion and gratitude, and you will see joy and serenity become an integral part of your daily life.

Elevating our mood: techniques for embracing happiness

Here are some practical techniques that you can apply to elevate your mood and increase your happiness on a daily basis:

a) Gratitude in action: perform acts of kindness and generosity towards others. It can be as simple as giving a sincere compliment, helping a neighbor or collaborating in a charitable cause. In doing so, you will not only bring joy to others, but you will also cultivate a deep sense of satisfaction and fulfillment in your own life.

b) The power of smiles: try smiling more often, even when you are not feeling particularly happy. Smiling has the power to trigger a positive response in our brain, releasing endorphins and creating a sense of well-being. In addition, your smile can spread to others and create an atmosphere of joy around you.

c) The exploration of *flow*: find activities in which you immerse yourself completely, where time seems to vanish and you feel totally absorbed. It can be painting, dancing, writing or any other activity that you are passionate about. As you enter this state of flow, you will experience deep satisfaction and a connection to your true self.

Practical exercises for embracing joy in daily life

Now, I invite you to participate in practical exercises that will help you incorporate joy into your daily life:

a) The happy moments journal: Take a few minutes each day to write in a journal the moments of happiness you experience. It could be a shared laugh with a loved one, a personal achievement, or a moment of connection with nature. By recording and reliving these moments, you will be training your mind to recognize and appreciate the joy present in your life.

b) Music as a mood elevator: create a playlist with songs that make you feel happy and fill you with positive energy. When you need a boost, put on your playlist and let yourself be carried away by the rhythm and melodies that will fill you with joy. Music has the power to elevate our mood and transform our day.

c) Nature as a source of inspiration: Take time to connect with nature. Stroll through a park, sit by a river or enjoy the fresh air in the mountains. Observe the beauty that surrounds you, listen to the sounds of nature and breathe deeply. Nature provides a haven of peace and serenity, and reminds us of the wonder of being alive.

Remember that happiness is not a final destination, but a path that we can embark on every day. By incorporating these techniques and exercises into your life, you will be taking significant steps towards a happier and more fulfilling life.

Finding meaning and purpose

I want to explore the powerful journey of finding meaning and purpose in our lives with you. It is a quest that connects us to our deepest selves and inspires us to live more fully and authentically.

Meaning and purpose are not found in faraway places or in great achievements. They are rooted in our daily experiences and in the way we choose to live our lives. Some reflections that can guide us on this path are:

Connect with your values: Reflect on the principles and beliefs that are important to you. What do you really value in life? Identifying your values will give you an internal compass to guide your decisions and actions.

Find your passions: Think about the activities that make you feel alive and excited - what are you passionate about? Whether it's music, art, nature or helping others, finding your passions brings you closer to your true purpose.

Discover your strengths: We all have unique talents and abilities. Take a moment to reflect on your strengths and how you can use them to make a difference in the world. Recognizing your gifts helps you unlock your potential and contribute in a meaningful way.

Find deeper meaning in your daily activities: Sometimes, we can find meaning and purpose in the simplest tasks. Ask yourself how you can infuse intention and mindfulness into what you do on a daily basis. Whether it's cooking, working, interacting with others or taking care of yourself, you'll find greater satisfaction in recognizing the intrinsic value of each moment.

Remember that meaning and purpose are not static, but evolve over time. Allow yourself to explore, experiment and adjust your course according to your inner discoveries. By embracing this journey of self-knowledge and connection, you will move closer and closer to a life filled with meaning and purpose.

Each of us has the capacity to find our own path to fulfillment and fulfillment. As we go on this journey together, I encourage you to allow yourself to explore, learn and grow.

Meaning and purpose are waiting to be discovered within you, and I am here to accompany you in this wonderful process of self-discovery.

CHAPTER 6

Self-care: your journey to wellness

Embracing self-care: a path to stress reduction

Self-care is the conscious act of dedicating time and energy to taking care of ourselves, both physically and emotionally. When we immerse ourselves in the world of self-care and discover how to prioritize our well-being, we can make a big difference in our daily lives.

We know that stress can have an overwhelming impact on our lives. However, by incorporating self-care practices, we can counteract its negative effects and find a healthy balance.

Self-care becomes a beacon of light that guides us towards calm, serenity and personal renewal.

Nurturing yourself: techniques for practicing self-care and self-love

Self-care and self-love are fundamental pillars for our well-being. Here are some inspiring techniques that you can implement in your daily life:

a) Time for you: set aside special moments in your schedule to do the things that make you happy. It could be reading a book you are passionate about, enjoying a relaxing bath or simply taking a walk in nature. Remember, your time is valuable and you deserve to pamper yourself.

b) Balanced diet: pay attention to what you put on your plate. Prioritize a healthy and balanced diet, full of fresh and nutritious food. Also, don't forget to hydrate properly to keep your body and mind in optimal condition.

c) Gratitude practice: Take a few minutes each day to reflect on the things you are grateful for. You can keep a gratitude journal where you write down three positive things that happened in your day. This simple exercise will help you cultivate an attitude of appreciation and focus on the good things around you.

Practical exercises to integrate self-care into your daily routine

It's time to take action and bring self-care into your daily routine. Here are some practical exercises you can implement:

a) Conscious breathing: take breaks during the day to practice conscious breathing. Inhale deeply, feeling the air fill your lungs, and then exhale slowly, letting go of any tension or worries. This simple practice will help you reduce stress and connect with your present.

b) Movement that fills you with vitality: find a form of movement that makes you feel good. It can be yoga, dancing, walking or any physical activity you enjoy. Exercise will not only strengthen your body, but it will also release endorphins, the happy hormones, and give you a sense of empowerment and well-being.

c) Self-compassion: give yourself permission to make mistakes and learn from them. Treat yourself with kindness and understanding, just as you would a loved one. Self-care also involves forgiving yourself when necessary and reminding yourself that you are enough just the way you are.

Self-care is not selfishness but an investment in your own happiness and well-being. By prioritizing and taking care of yourself, you will be better equipped to face life's challenges and offer your best self to the world around you.

Cultivating inner serenity through the power of meditation

When I seek moments of peace and tranquility in my life, I always turn to the practice of meditation. Meditation is a powerful tool that allows us to cultivate inner serenity and find balance in the midst of daily chaos. Through dedication and constant practice, we can create an inner space of calm and serenity that accompanies us every step of the way.

Meditation is much more than sitting in silence with your legs crossed and eyes closed. It is an opportunity to connect with ourselves, to explore our inner world and find answers to our deepest concerns. By immersing ourselves in meditative practice, we give ourselves the freedom to let go of worries and distractions, and focus on the present.

In the stillness of meditation, we find a refuge where we can release accumulated stress and tension. It is as if we are leaving behind the noise of the outside world and entering a sacred space of introspection and self-knowledge. Here, in this corner of serenity, we can nourish our being and recharge our energies.

The practice of meditation invites us to be present in the here and now, to observe our thoughts without judging them and to accept our emotions as they are. It helps us to cultivate mindfulness and develop greater mental clarity.

As we immerse ourselves in inner stillness, we find that our thoughts slowly fade away, leaving space for a sense of peace and deep connection.

By meditating, we learn to listen to the whisper of our intuition, that wise and compassionate voice that guides us on our path. We become observant of our inner experiences and find new perspectives and solutions to the challenges we face. Meditation gives us the opportunity to know ourselves on a deeper level and to cultivate compassion for ourselves and others.

The beauty of meditation is that it does not require special skills or a long time. You can start with just a few minutes a day and gradually increase the length of your practice. Find a quiet place where you feel comfortable and adopt a relaxed posture. Close your eyes and direct your attention to your breathing, allowing your mind to gradually quiet down.

As you become more familiar with meditation, you can explore different approaches and techniques to suit your needs. You can experiment with guided meditation, where an instructor walks you through visualizations and positive affirmations. Or you can opt for silent meditation, where you immerse yourself in silence and inner stillness.

Remember that meditation is a personal and unique journey. There is no right or wrong way to do it. The important thing is to take time for yourself, to reconnect with yourself and to cultivate the inner serenity you long for. Allow yourself to explore and discover the transformative power of meditation in your life.

So I invite you to take a few moments each day to dedicate yourself to yourself, to breathe deeply and to immerse yourself in the wonderful practice of meditation.

Allow your inner self to blossom and discover the full potential within you. We deserve this time of care and serenity. Together, we can find the balance and tranquility we long for.

Exploring your passions: finding joy and satisfaction in what you love to do.

When you immerse yourself in what you are truly passionate about, the world lights up in a special way. Finding that inner spark, that fire that burns deep within you, is a wonderful gift that life gives you. And in this journey of self-discovery, I want to accompany you and encourage you to explore your passions, to find joy and satisfaction in what you love to do.

Each of us possesses a unique set of interests, talents and curiosities. Sometimes these gifts remain hidden under the demands of daily life, external expectations and the responsibilities we carry on our shoulders. But I say to you that it is vital to allow ourselves to explore and nurture those passions that make us feel alive and fulfilled.

Do you remember the last time you lost yourself in an activity you love? It can be something as simple as painting, writing, singing, dancing or cooking. When you engage in what you are truly passionate about, you experience a sense of flow and well-being, as if you are in harmony with the universe. That's the magic of following your passions.

You may be asking yourself: "How can I discover my true passions?" The answer lies within you. Allow yourself to explore different activities, without judging or limiting yourself by external standards. Notice which activities make you feel excited, very well make you lose track of time and very well awaken your creativity and enthusiasm. Listen to your heart and follow the glimmers of happiness that come your way.

Sometimes our passions may seem insignificant or impractical compared to social or professional expectations. But I want to remind you that your happiness and well-being are valuable. Don't be afraid to embrace your passions, even if they don't fit into established molds. You deserve to live an authentic and fulfilling life, and pursuing your passions is a fundamental part of that journey.

By following your passions, you give yourself permission to be yourself in all your splendor. You experience a sense of purpose and meaning that transcends the challenges and obstacles you may face. Your passions nurture you, empower you and bring you deep inner satisfaction.

It doesn't matter if you dedicate a few hours a week or if you can make your passion your profession. The important thing is that you set aside regular time to cultivate that special connection with what you love to do. It can be a moment of peace and joy amidst the hustle and bustle of everyday life.

I invite you to give yourself permission to follow your passions, to explore that inner world of creativity and authenticity. Together, we will discover the beauty and fulfillment that comes from living a life in harmony with our true passions. We deserve to experience that joy and fulfillment every step of the way.

So go ahead, immerse yourself in what you love to do. Explore your passions, allow them to blossom and take yourself to new heights of happiness and fulfillment. The world is waiting for you to shine in all your splendor!

The art of saying "no": setting healthy boundaries in your life

In this hectic and demanding modern life, we often find ourselves caught up in a collection of commitments and demands that drain us physically and emotionally. We always seem to be saying "yes" to everything and everyone, leaving little room to take care of ourselves.

But let me tell you something: learning the art of saying "no" is an act of self-love and a powerful tool for setting healthy boundaries in our lives.

Often, we feel obligated to please others and meet the expectations they impose on us. We worry that we will disappoint or be judged if we refuse something. However, by consciously and respectfully saying "no," we give ourselves permission to take care of our own needs and priorities.

Understanding that saying "no" does not imply selfishness, but rather authenticity and self-care, is liberating. It allows us to set boundaries that protect our energy, mental and emotional health. When we refuse to take on more than we can handle, we make room for what really matters in our lives.

It is important to remember that time and energy are valuable resources. Every time we say "yes" to something, we are saying "no" to other things that might be more aligned with our personal purposes and desires. By setting healthy boundaries, we give ourselves the opportunity to focus on what really matters to us and makes us happy.

Saying "no" is not easy, but it's not impossible either. Start by connecting with yourself and listening to your deepest needs and desires. Reflect on your priorities and value your time and energy. As you become more familiar with your own boundaries, you will find it easier to express them assertively and respectfully.

Remember that you don't have to give detailed explanations when you say "no". You can be honest and clear, with no need to apologize. Allow yourself to say "no" with kindness and firmness, knowing that you are taking care of yourself in the best possible way.

By setting healthy boundaries, we are also teaching others to respect our needs and desires. We empower ourselves by affirming our value and demonstrating that we deserve balance in our lives. In doing so, we inspire others to do the same and cultivate more authentic and respectful relationships.

I invite you to explore the art of saying "no" with courage and compassion. Allow yourself to establish healthy habits that protect you and allow you to flourish. Together, we can learn to prioritize our own happiness and well-being, while building more authentic and nurturing relationships.

You deserve a balanced and joyful life!

The role of sleep in self-care: tips to improve your night's sleep

Sleep is one of the fundamental pillars of self-care and well-being. During those hours of rest at night, our body and mind are renewed, rejuvenated and prepared to face a new day full of energy and vitality. That's why it's so important to make sure we get quality sleep. Let me share with you some tips to improve your night's rest and wake up every morning feeling refreshed and revitalized.

First, establish a consistent sleep routine. Try to go to bed and get up at the same time every day, even on weekends. This will help regulate your internal clock and establish a healthy sleep pattern. Also, avoid caffeine and heavy food before bedtime, as they can interfere with the quality of your sleep.

Create an environment conducive to sleep in your bedroom. Keep the place cool, dark and quiet. If necessary, use earplugs or a sleep mask. Also, consider using gentle aromatherapy, such as lavender, to promote relaxation and tranquility. Your bedroom should be your restful sanctuary, a place where you can unwind and rejuvenate.

Turn off electronic devices at least one hour before bedtime. The blue light emitted by screens can disrupt your circadian rhythm and make it difficult to sleep. Instead, opt for relaxing activities such as reading a book, listening to soft music or practicing meditation. These activities will help you unwind and prepare your mind and body for a restful sleep.

Practice sleep hygiene. This involves establishing a series of routines and habits that promote optimal rest. For example, avoid long naps during the day, as they can interfere with your nighttime sleep. Also, make sure you have a comfortable, quality mattress and pillows that give you the proper support to rest fully.

If you find it difficult to fall asleep or if you suffer from insomnia, consider practicing relaxation techniques, such as deep breathing or guided imagery. These tools can help calm your mind and prepare you for a restful, restorative sleep.

Remember that sleep is a vital part of our self-care. It is the time when our body regenerates and strengthens, and our mind finds the clarity and balance it needs. Don't underestimate the power of restful sleep.

So I invite you to prioritize your night's rest and incorporate these tips into your daily routine. Allow yourself the luxury of disconnecting, of nourishing yourself with deep and restorative sleep.

Together, we can create a healthy sleep habit that gives us the energy and vitality we need to face each day with serenity and joy. Get a good night's rest and wake up to the world with a radiant smile!

Establishing technology-free spaces for self-care

In this digital age we live in, we are constantly connected through our technological devices. While technology brings us many advantages and conveniences, it can also be overwhelming and taxing on our minds and emotional well-being.

That is why it is crucial to establish technology-free spaces in our daily lives, to cultivate self-care and find balance in a hyper-connected world.

Digital disconnection does not mean giving up technology completely, but rather finding a healthy balance between the virtual world and the real world. It allows us to take a break from constant digital stimulation and reconnect with ourselves and the present.

When we unplug, we give our mind and body permission to rest and recharge. We free ourselves from the stress and anxiety that often accompany the constant bombardment of notifications, emails and social media. We give ourselves the opportunity to live in the present moment, to enjoy the little things in life and to reconnect with our deepest emotions and needs.

Establishing technology-free spaces may seem challenging at first, but it is a worthwhile act of self-love and self-care.

Some ideas to get you started

Create sacred technology-free moments: dedicate certain times of the day or week to be completely disconnected. It can be an hour before bedtime, one day a week or even a weekend technology retreat. Use that time to do activities that nourish you and bring you peace, such as reading a book, taking a walk outdoors, practicing yoga or simply being present at the moment.

Set technological limits: define specific times when you will disconnect from your devices, such as during meals, family gatherings or moments of relaxation. Turn off notifications and set limits on social media use. Allow yourself to be fully present in your interactions and enjoy the company of others.

Create a technology-free sanctuary: designate a space in your home where you can completely disconnect. It can be a meditation corner, a reading room or even your bedroom. Decorate that space in a cozy, electronics-free way. Use it as a sacred place to relax, reflect and connect with yourself.

Remember that the goal is not to get completely away from technology, but to find a healthy and conscious balance in its use. Digital disconnection allows us to prioritize our mental health, our creativity and our relationships.

I encourage you to give yourself the gift of disconnecting and establishing technology-free spaces in your life.

CHAPTER 7

Positive affirmations: strengthening your transformational mindset

Inner dialogue: the impact of words on your mental health

Positive affirmations are powerful tools that allow us to reprogram our minds, free ourselves from negative thought patterns and cultivate a positive and empowering mindset.

We will discover the incredible power that words have over our minds and how we can use them to transform our mindset and reach our full potential.

Imagine for a moment that your thoughts are seeds that you plant in the garden of your mind. What kind of seeds are you planting? Are they seeds of self-criticism, doubt and negativity? Or, conversely, are they seeds of confidence, self-love and optimism?

Our internal dialogue has a profound impact on our mental health. If we constantly repeat negative messages to ourselves, our mind internalizes them and begins to believe them as absolute truths.

But here's the good news: we can change that internal dialogue and create a fertile mental environment for personal growth and happiness.

Affirmations of success: the art of formulating and applying positive thoughts.

Formulating affirmations of success and positivity is a skill we can develop. Here are some effective methods for creating and applying affirmations in your daily life:

a) Be specific and present: formulate your affirmations clearly and in the present moment. For example, instead of saying, "Someday you will be successful", say "I am a successful person and right now I have the power to create my own success".

b) Feel the emotion: when repeating your affirmations, connect with the emotion they would generate if they were to become a reality. Visualize yourself experiencing the success and happiness you wish to achieve. In doing so, you are sending powerful signals to your mind and heart.

c) Repeat and reaffirm: repeat your affirmations daily, both out loud and silently. You can write them on cards and carry them with you, place them in visible places or even record them on your phone to listen to them on the go. Constant repetition will strengthen your beliefs and bring you closer to your goals.

Exercises for integrating positive affirmations into your daily life

Now is the time to put positive affirmations into practice in your daily life. Here are some exercises you can do:

a) Confidence mirror: every day, in front of a mirror, look deeply into your eyes and repeat affirmations of self-love and self-confidence: "I am strong", "I am abundant", "I am patient", "I am sufficient", etc. Watch your reflection transform into a confident and valuable person. This simple but powerful exercise will help you cultivate strong self-esteem.

b) Empowering mantras: identify a lasting one that resonates with you and make it a personal mantra. Repeat it in times of challenge or insecurity to remind you of your inner strength and worth.

c) Affirmation journal: write your positive affirmations in a journal every night before you go to sleep. Reflect on how they made you feel during the day and record the small accomplishments you have achieved because of them. This journal will be a valuable tool for self-empowerment and personal growth.

Positive affirmations have the power to transform our mindset and elevate our quality of life. By integrating them into our daily routine, we are building a solid foundation of self-love, confidence and success.

Let yourself believe in yourself and be the protagonist of your own story!

Affirmations for self-care: cultivating a loving relationship with yourself

When it comes to self-care, cultivating a loving and compassionate relationship with yourself is critical. Recognizing your worth and giving yourself the love and care you deserve is a powerful step toward inner serenity and emotional balance. Positive affirmations can be a wonderful tool to strengthen this relationship and nurture your overall well-being.

Let me share with you some affirmations for self-care that you can incorporate into your daily life. Remember that these affirmations are based on the premise that you deserve love, care and respect, and that you can offer these to yourself:

"I love and accept myself as I am, with all my virtues and my imperfections. I am worthy of love and respect.

"I take care of my body and mind with love and gratitude. I am committed to maintaining healthy habits that nourish and strengthen me."

"My emotional well-being is a priority in my life. It allows me to feel and process my emotions in a healthy and compassionate way."

"I give myself permission to set healthy boundaries in all areas of my life. I recognize that saying 'no' when necessary is an act of self-love."

"I treat myself with kindness and compassion in every situation. I speak to myself with words of encouragement and support."

"Self-care is an investment in my happiness and inner peace. I give myself time to rest, relax and rejuvenate."

"I am deserving of moments of pleasure and fun. I allow myself to enjoy the things that make me happy without guilt or judgment."

"I appreciate and celebrate my uniqueness. I allow myself to be authentic and live according to my values and desires."

"I surround myself with people and environments that support and inspire me. I choose relationships and environments that nurture my personal growth."

"I forgive myself for my past mistakes and allow myself to grow and learn. Every day is an opportunity to start over."

You can repeat these affirmations in moments of calm and reflection, or you can write them in an affirmation journal as a way of reminding yourself of your worth and fostering self-love. Remember that cultivating a loving relationship with yourself is an ongoing process, and these affirmations can be a constant guide on your journey toward self-care and inner serenity.

I encourage you to embrace yourself with love and acceptance, and to remind yourself daily that you deserve the best care you can give yourself. You are valuable, worthy of love and deserve to live a full and authentic life. Together, we can cultivate a self-care relationship based on love and compassion for ourselves.

Resilience affirmations: strengthening your mindset in the face of life's challenges

When faced with life's challenges, it is essential to cultivate a resilient mindset. Resilience enables us to overcome obstacles, adapt to change and remain strong in the face of adversity. Positive affirmations can be a powerful tool to strengthen our resilience and face challenges with confidence and determination.

Let me share with you some affirmations for resilience that you can integrate into your daily life. Remember that these affirmations are designed to strengthen your mindset and help you find strength in difficult times:

"I am capable of overcoming any challenge that comes my way. I am confident in my ability to find solutions and move forward."

"Every obstacle is an opportunity to grow and learn. I am open to the lessons that life presents to me."

"I am strong and courageous. My inner strength guides me through difficult situations and drives me forward."

"My past does not define my future. I have the power to create a life full of possibilities and success."

"I trust myself and my intuition. I have the wisdom to make the right decisions and follow the right path."

"Adversity doesn't defeat me, it strengthens me. Every challenge I face makes me more resilient and brings me closer to the strongest version of myself."

"Life is full of ups and downs, but I am able to adapt and find balance in any circumstance."

"Fear does not control me. I choose to face my fears with courage and turn them into opportunities for personal growth."

"I trust the process of life. Even if things don't always go as I plan, I know that everything happens for a reason and I can find meaning in every experience."

"I am a magnet for positive opportunities. The universe conspires in my favor and gives me the tools I need to overcome any challenge."

Remember that resilience is strengthened by constant practice. Repeat these affirmations in times of doubt or difficulty, and allow them to remind you of your own ability to overcome any obstacle. As we cultivate a resilient mindset, we become capable of facing challenges with confidence and finding growth and success in every experience.

You are stronger than you think and are destined to overcome any obstacle that comes your way. Together, we can cultivate a resilient mindset and face life's challenges with courage and determination.

How to create your own affirmation book

Creating your own book of affirmations is a wonderful way to strengthen your positive mindset and nurture your personal growth. By writing and repeating meaningful affirmations, you can transform your thinking and boost your self-confidence. Let me guide you through this process so you can create your own personalized and inspirational book of affirmations.

Find a quiet time and place: Find a time when you can be calm and undistracted. Choose a quiet space where you feel comfortable and relaxed so you can focus intensely on this process.

Reflect on your goals and desires: Before you begin writing your affirmations, take a moment to reflect on your goals, desires and areas of your life that you want to focus on. Ask yourself what aspects you want to strengthen and what positive changes you want to manifest.

Formulate positive affirmations: now is the time to start writing your affirmations. Remember that they must be positive, in the present tense and formulated in the first person. For example, instead of saying, "I want to be happy", you can say "I am worthy of happiness and I attract it into my life". Be specific and focus on the aspects you want to change or improve.

Be authentic and connect with your emotions: As you write your affirmations, it is important that they are authentic and resonate with you on an emotional level. Connect with your deepest desires and express them in words that inspire and motivate you.

Organize your affirmation book: You can organize your affirmations in any way you prefer. You can group them by categories such as self-love, success, health, relationships, etc. You can also choose a specific order that makes sense to you. Remember that this book is personal and should reflect your needs and preferences.

Repeat your affirmations daily: Once you have created your book of affirmations, it is time to put them into practice. Set aside time each day to read your affirmations out loud. You can do this in the morning to start the day with a positive mindset, or before bed to set a powerful intention before you rest.

Feel free to adapt and update your affirmations: as you move forward on your personal journey, it is natural for your goals and desires to evolve. If you feel the need to adjust or add new affirmations, feel free to do so. Your affirmation book is a reflection of your constant growth and change.

Remember that the power of affirmations lies in constant repetition and believing in their truth. As you immerse yourself in the process of creating and reading your affirmations, your mindset will strengthen and how you move closer to the life you desire. Enjoy this creative process and trust in the transformative power of your own words.

Together, we can create a life full of positivity, growth and well-being. Go ahead, start writing your own book of affirmations and unleash your full potential!

CHAPTER 8

Cognitive behavioral therapy (CBT): navigating your thoughts and emotions

Understanding CBT: The Power of Personal Transformation

Cognitive behavioral therapy is a form of psychological therapy based on the premise that our thoughts influence our emotions and behaviors.

This therapy helps us identify negative and dysfunctional thought patterns and replaces them with more realistic and constructive thoughts. In doing so, we can reduce stress, improve our self-esteem and strengthen our emotional resilience.

Tools for navigating your thoughts: transforming the negative into the positive

CBT provides us with a variety of practical techniques to understand and modify our negative thought patterns. Here are some of them:

a) Challenging thoughts: Closely examine those automatic negative thoughts that arise in your mind. Question their validity and look for evidence to support or refute those beliefs. For example, if you have the thought, "I can never do anything well," look for evidence of times when you have succeeded and done well.

b) Cognitive restructuring: once the negative thought patterns are identified, replace them with more realistic and positive thoughts. For example, if you have the thought, "I always make mistakes", you can replace it with "Making mistakes is part of learning and I can learn and grow from them".

c) Mindfulness: practice mindfulness to be aware of the present moment without judgment. This allows you to observe your thoughts and emotions without identifying with them. In doing so, you will develop greater mental clarity and the ability to respond in a more conscious and calm manner.

Practical exercises to apply CBT in your daily life

Now is the time to put these CBT techniques into practice in your daily life. Here are some exercises you can do:

a) Thought Log: keep a record of your automatic negative thoughts during the day. Write down the thought, the triggering situation and the associated emotions. Then use cognitive training and challenging techniques to transform those negative thoughts into more positive and realistic thoughts.

b) Gratitude journal: every night, write down three things for which you are grateful. This will help you train your mind to focus on the positive and develop an attitude of gratitude in your life.

c) Positive self-affirmations: create a list of positive affirmations that empower and motivate you. Repeat them out loud every day, especially in times of doubt or challenge. For example, you can say to yourself, "I am valuable and capable of overcoming any obstacle that comes my way."

CBT is an ongoing process of self-exploration and transformation. As you immerse yourself in this journey, be patient with yourself and celebrate each small step you take toward a more positive and healthy mindset.

Identifying and questioning your limiting beliefs: overcoming mental barriers

Let's continue with our exciting journey of self-discovery and self-improvement. It is time to learn about the process of identifying and questioning our limiting beliefs. These beliefs are like little inner voices that tell us what we can and cannot achieve, and often prevent us from reaching our full potential.

Do you ever get stuck in negative thought patterns? Have you ever wondered why you sabotage yourself when it comes to pursuing your goals and dreams? Well, the answer may lie in your limiting beliefs. These beliefs, often rooted in past experiences or outside influences, can act as mental roadblocks, preventing you from moving forward toward a full and satisfying life.

But don't worry, you are on the road to personal transformation and self-improvement. Here I will guide you through the process of identifying those limiting beliefs and questioning their validity. How will we do it? Through a series of practical steps and deep reflections, I will help you unearth those beliefs and challenge them from a more objective and realistic perspective.

First, we will immerse ourselves in a process of self-exploration. Together, we will examine the beliefs rooted in your mind and heart. I invite you to reflect on the ideas that you have been repeating to yourself for a long time. Are there recurring thoughts that limit you? What keeps you from believing in your own potential?

Once you have identified your limiting beliefs, it is time to question their validity. Are these beliefs really true? Are they based on solid facts or are they simply unfounded assumptions? I encourage you to critically analyze each belief and find evidence to support or contradict its veracity.

Remember, this process is not about denying your past experiences or minimizing your challenges. It's about freeing yourself from the mental ties that prevent you from growing and achieving your goals. It is an exercise in self-compassion and authenticity, allowing you to challenge those beliefs and replace them with more empowering and positive thoughts.

In this journey, you will not be alone, we all have areas in which we can grow and excel, and together we can build a strong and resilient mindset. Allow yourself to believe in yourself and your ability to overcome mental obstacles. I am here to support you every step of the way and celebrate your achievements.

You are capable of transforming your life and achieving the fulfillment you deserve!

Cognitive restructuring techniques: transforming negative thought patterns

We have all experienced times when our thoughts become dark and pessimistic. Those negative thought patterns can affect our self-esteem, our relationships and our outlook on life in general. But the good news is that we don't have to get stuck in those patterns. We can learn to challenge them and replace them with more positive and realistic thoughts.

Cognitive reconstruction is a powerful tool that allows us to examine and challenge the automatic negative thoughts that arise in our minds. It helps us identify cognitive distortions, those biased ways of thinking that lead us to negative and unrealistic conclusions about ourselves and the world around us.

There are several cognitive-building techniques that allow you to challenge and change those negative thought patterns. These techniques will help you build a more positive, realistic and compassionate mindset towards yourself and others.

The first thing we must do is learn to identify automatic negative thoughts, this is a crucial step in the process of cognitive construction. These thoughts are those that arise quickly and automatically in our mind, often without us realizing it, some strategies you can employ to recognize and identify these negative thoughts are:

Pay attention to your emotions: automatic negative thoughts are usually accompanied by negative emotions such as sadness, anxiety or anger. If you feel bad emotionally, relax and observe what thoughts are going through your mind at that moment.

Be aware of recurring patterns: Throughout the day, notice if there are any negative thoughts that recur frequently. It may be constant self-criticism, anticipation of negative outcomes, or fear of failure. These patterns are indicators of negative automatic thoughts.

Watch for generalizations and extreme words: automatic negative thoughts tend to be absolute and exaggerated. Words like "always," "never," "everything," or "no one" are signs that you are dealing with automatic negative thinking. For example, thinking, "I never get anything right" or "I'm always wrong".

Listen to your internal dialogue: pay attention to how you talk to yourself in challenging or stressful situations. If you find that your thoughts are self-critical, pessimistic or discouraging, you are probably dealing with automatic negative thoughts.

Record your thoughts: Keeping a thought journal can be helpful in identifying negative thought patterns. Write down thoughts that arise in different situations and how they make you feel. This will help you detect automatic negative thoughts and examine them more clearly.

Remember that the goal is not to judge or criticize your thoughts, but simply to be aware of them. Once you identify automatic negative thoughts, you can question their veracity and replace them with more realistic and positive thoughts. It is a gradual process, but with practice and perseverance, you can transform your thinking and cultivate a healthier, more constructive mindset.

When you find yourself facing automatic negative thoughts, it is important to question their veracity and look for evidence to support or contradict those beliefs. Some strategies that have helped me in these cases can also help you:

Examine the evidence: ask yourself if there is concrete evidence to support your automatic negative thinking. Are there specific facts or events that prove your thinking is true? If you cannot find solid evidence, it is possible that your thinking is distorted.

Look for alternative perspectives: try to find different ways of looking at the situation. Are there other possible interpretations that are not so negative? Consider different points of view and ask yourself if there is evidence to support these alternative perspectives.

Analyze past experiences: reflect on similar situations in the past. Are there examples that contradict your automatic negative thinking? Recall times when you have been successful or when things didn't turn out as badly as you feared. Use those experiences as evidence that your automatic negative thoughts may not be completely accurate.

Evaluate the logic of your thoughts: examine the logic behind your automatic negative thoughts. Does your reasoning make sense? Are you applying a double standard or exaggerating the importance of certain aspects? Try to be objective and analyze whether your thoughts are coherent and realistic.

Ask for feedback from others you trust: sometimes, we can lose objectivity when analyzing our own thoughts. Seek the opinion of close friends or loved ones you trust. They can provide you with a more balanced perspective and help you evaluate the veracity of your automatic negative thoughts.

Develop positive and realistic affirmations: create positive affirmations that counteract your automatic negative thoughts. For example, if your negative thought is "I am a failure," replace it with "I am learning and growing with every experience." Use affirmations that push you, motivate you, and remind you of your strengths and capabilities.

Practice self-reflection and gratitude: take time to reflect on your accomplishments, strengths and positive things in your life. Practice gratitude and focus on the good things around you. This will help you shift your perspective to a more positive and realistic one.

Practice mindfulness and self-care: Mindfulness helps you to be present in the present moment and observe your thoughts without judgment. In addition, taking care of yourself physically and emotionally will contribute to a more positive and healthy state of mind.

Remember that challenging your automatic negative thoughts takes practice and patience. It is not about denying your emotions, but about analyzing and challenging thoughts that may be distorted or exaggerated.

As you practice this skill, you will find it easier to find evidence to support more realistic and constructive thinking. Be kind to yourself during this process and celebrate every little bit of progress you make. With consistent practice, you will be able to cultivate a more realistic and positive mindset.

Now, at this point, you may be asking yourself: what techniques can help me replace automatic negative thoughts with more realistic and positive thoughts?

There are several specific techniques for this, such as the alternative thinking technique, in which you will learn to replace negative thoughts with more realistic and positive thoughts; the self-reinforcement technique, which consists of recognizing and celebrating your achievements and strengths to strengthen your self-confidence and self-esteem; the external perspective technique, which will help you examine negative thoughts from an objective and more compassionate perspective.

Remember that everyone is different, so it is important to find the techniques that work best for you. You can try different approaches and adapt them to your needs and preferences. The key is consistent practice and patience with yourself to achieve a positive change in your thinking patterns.

Learning to manage your emotions: emotional regulation through CBT

Emotions are a natural part of our human experience. At times, they can be intense and overwhelming, which can hinder our ability to function effectively in our daily lives. However, through Cognitive Behavioral Therapy (CBT), we can learn to manage and regulate them in a healthy way.

This can be achieved thanks to effective strategies and techniques for emotional regulation, which will allow us to find serenity and balance in our lives, I can briefly mention some of them:

Recognizing and labeling emotions: the first step in emotional regulation is to be aware of our emotions. Learning to identify and label our emotions allows us to understand what we are experiencing. We can use words such as "sadness," "anger," or "joy" to describe how we feel. By recognizing our emotions, we can begin to work on managing them.

Practicing mindfulness: Mindfulness helps us to be present at the moment and accept our emotions without judging them. By practicing mindfulness, we connect with our emotions without letting them drag us down. We can use techniques such as mindful breathing, meditation or observing our thoughts and feelings to cultivate mindfulness.

Challenging negative thoughts and beliefs: our thoughts can influence our emotions. CBT teaches us to challenge and replace negative or distorted thoughts that may be contributing to our negative emotions. We can change our perspective and experience more balanced emotions by challenging these limiting beliefs.

Develop problem-solving skills: Many times, our intense emotions are related to challenging situations in our lives. Through CBT, we can learn problem-solving skills to address these situations effectively. This involves identifying challenges, generating solution options, and taking concrete actions to solve problems and reduce emotional stress.

Cultivate self-care: Self-care plays a crucial role in emotional regulation. It is important to devote time and attention to our physical, emotional and mental needs. This can include activities such as exercising regularly, maintaining a healthy diet, getting enough sleep, pursuing hobbies that we enjoy and surrounding ourselves with positive and supportive relationships.

Remember that emotional regulation is a gradual process and requires practice. Each person is unique, so it is important to find the strategies that work best for you. Through CBT, we can learn to manage our emotions in a healthy way and cultivate a balanced and satisfying emotional life...

Challenging cognitive biases: broadening your perspective and mental flexibility

On our path to balance and tranquility, it is essential to explore and challenge the cognitive biases that can limit the way we think and perceive the world. These biases are automatic patterns of thinking that lead us to interpret reality in a distorted way.

However, through Cognitive Behavioral Therapy (CBT), we can broaden our perspective and develop greater mental flexibility.

Awareness of cognitive biases: The first step in challenging cognitive biases is to recognize their existence. Constructive self-criticism allows us to observe our thinking patterns and detect possible distortions. By being aware of these biases, we can take steps to counteract their influence on the way we perceive reality.

Questioning automatic interpretations: Cognitive biases often lead to automatic and hasty interpretations of events. It is critical to question these interpretations and consider other possible perspectives. Ask yourself, "Is there another way to look at this situation?" "What is the evidence to support my interpretation?" and "Are there alternatives that I am not considering?".

Example: Imagine that you have had a bad experience in a job interview and automatically think, "I am a failure and will never get a good job." By challenging this automatic interpretation, you might consider other factors that could have influenced the interview, such as nerves or lack of specific experience. This allows you to take a more balanced and realistic perspective.

Evidence testing: Cognitive biases are often based on unfounded assumptions or generalizations. To counteract them, it is useful to look for evidence that supports or contradicts our automatic thoughts. Examine past experiences, look for concrete examples and analyze whether your beliefs are based on real facts or simply distorted perceptions.

Example: if you have the automatic belief "No one appreciates me," you might look for evidence to support or contradict this belief. You might recall times when friends or loved ones have expressed appreciation or praised you. This evidence will help you challenge the automatic belief and recognize that you are valued by others.

Exploring different perspectives: Cognitive biases lead us to see the world from a single, limited perspective. To broaden our vision, it is important to consider different points of view and open ourselves to new interpretations of events. This allows us to gain mental flexibility and develop a more complete understanding of situations.

Example: if you have a tendency to polarization (seeing things in terms of black or white, all or nothing), try to consider the different gradations and nuances that may exist in a situation. Ask yourself, "Is there a possible middle ground?", "How might this situation be viewed from the perspective of others?"

By challenging cognitive biases and expanding our thinking, we can free ourselves from the limitations they impose on us. CBT gives us the tools we need to explore new mental horizons and experience a richer, more enriching reality.

Remember that this process requires practice and patience, but the benefits will be significant on your path to inner serenity and emotional balance.

CHAPTER 9

Energy in motion: a vital link between physical and mental health

The transformative power of exercise: a boost to mental health

Let me share a powerful secret with you: physical exercise not only strengthens our muscles, but also our mental health. When we move, we release endorphins, the happiness hormones, which fill us with energy and make us feel good.

In addition, regular exercise has been shown to reduce stress, anxiety and depression, while improving our self-esteem and our ability to cope with daily challenges.

Awakening the warrior within: strategies for integrating movement into your daily routine

Ready to take the first step toward an active and vibrant life? Here are some techniques to help you incorporate movement in a fun and rewarding way:

a) Find your passion: discover a physical activity that you are passionate about. It could be dancing, walking in nature, practicing yoga or playing a sport. By choosing something you enjoy, you will be motivated and encouraged to participate in it periodically.

b) Break the routine: vary your exercise routines to avoid boredom and stay motivated. Try new fitness classes, home workout challenges or outdoor activities. Diversity will bring a new level of excitement and enthusiasm to your active life.

c) Walk at every opportunity: Take every opportunity to walk more in your daily life. Park your car farther away, use the stairs instead of the elevator, and take short walks during your breaks. The simple act of walking can have a positive impact on your physical and mental health.

Practical exercises to stay active and reduce stress

It's time to get up and move!

Here are some practical exercises you can incorporate into your routine:

a) Interval training: alternate between bursts of high intensity and periods of rest. You can do this by running, jumping rope or using a stationary bike. This type of training increases your endurance, burns calories and improves your mood.

b) Morning Yoga: Take a few minutes each morning to practice a short yoga sequence. Stretch your body, breathe deeply and connect with your inner self. This gentle practice will help you start the day with calmness and mental clarity.

c) Dance as therapy: put on your favorite music and let yourself go with the rhythm. Dancing is not only fun, but it also releases tension and connects you with your most authentic expression. Don't worry about perfect steps, just enjoy the movement!
It's not about finding perfection in your exercise, it's about finding an activity that makes you feel good and keeps you active. Listen to your body and have fun while you move!
d) Go for a walk: If you don't have equipment, going for a walk may be the most suitable option for you. Once you have warmed up after five minutes of walking, increase your speed to 90-100% of your capacity for one minute, almost as if you were running. Then, after that minute, continue walking but reduce your speed to about 60% of your capacity for a minute or two. Repeat this process 5-10 times during the walk and you will get very positive benefits and results.

Exploring relaxing activities: other alternatives for stress reduction

The following are some other options that can help you to stay away from stress. Try practicing some of them, have fun and get rid of stress:
Swimming: immersing yourself in water and swimming can be a relaxing activity that combines physical exercise with a sense of calm and tranquility.

Tai Chi: this ancient Chinese practice combines gentle, flowing movements with deep breathing techniques and meditation. Tai Chi is known for its ability to reduce stress and promote relaxation.

Hiking: Connecting with nature through outdoor walks can have a calming effect on the mind and body. Exploring nature trails and breathing fresh air can help you release pent-up stress.

Pilates: This discipline focuses on strengthening muscles, improving posture and promoting body awareness. Controlled movements and attention to breathing can help reduce stress and increase relaxation.

Martial arts: practicing martial arts such as karate, taekwondo or judo not only improves physical condition, but also promotes concentration, self-control and the release of accumulated tensions.

Gardening: tending a garden or potting flowers can be a therapeutic activity that connects you with nature and allows you to enjoy quiet time outdoors.

Remember that everyone is different and may find stress relief in different activities. The important thing is to find what works best for you and enjoy the activities that allow you to maintain mental and physical balance.

Mental wellness activities: non-physical options for stress reduction

In our constant quest to find balance and tranquility, it is essential to remember that not all activities to combat stress have to be physical. In addition to taking care of our body, we must also take care of our minds and emotions.

Here are some non-physical options that can be of great help to reduce stress and cultivate our mental well-being.

Meditation and *Mindfulness*: the practice of meditation and *mindfulness* invites us to be present in the present moment, to observe our thoughts and emotions without judging them. Take a few minutes a day to sit in a quiet place, close your eyes and focus on your breathing. Observe how your thoughts come and go, without holding on to them. This practice will help you calm your mind and reduce stress.

Therapeutic writing: Taking a moment to write down your thoughts and emotions can be an excellent way to vent and process your experiences. Keep a personal journal where you can freely express your thoughts, reflections and concerns. You can also explore creative writing techniques, such as writing poetry or short stories, to unleash your creativity and find an escape from stress.

Art therapy: Art is a powerful tool for expressing and exploring your emotions. You can try different forms of artistic expression, such as painting, drawing, collage or even clay modeling. It doesn't matter if you are an expert or a beginner, the important thing is to let yourself be creative and enjoy the process. Art will allow you to release tensions and find a space of calm and self-discovery.

Inspirational reading: Immersing yourself in a good book can transport you to other worlds and provide inspiration and comfort. Choose books that address topics that interest you and inspire you to grow and develop personally. Whether you opt for novels, essays or self-help books, reading can be a wonderful way to unwind from everyday worries and immerse yourself in stories and insights that nourish your mind.

Listen to relaxing music: music has the power to influence our mood and relax our minds. Look for soft, soothing melodies that convey peace and tranquility. Take time to listen to music in a quiet environment, without distractions, and allow yourself to enjoy the sounds that caress your senses and help reduce stress.

Remember that these activities are complementary to physical practices that promote wellness. Incorporating these options into your daily routine will allow you to find a balance between body and mind, and help you reduce stress in a holistic way. Experiment with these activities and find out what works best for you.

I'm sure you'll find great relief and well-being in them!

CHAPTER 10

Conscious eating: nourishing body and mind for a full life

The power of food: nourishing our mental health

Let me share a secret with you: the foods we choose can be a powerful fuel for our mental health.

A balanced and nutritious diet not only strengthens our body, but also influences our cognitive and emotional processes.

Eating properly can improve our mood, increase our concentration and give us a greater sense of well-being in general.

Healing flavors: strategies for healthy and conscious eating.

It's time to discover the pleasure of eating consciously and healthily!

Here are some techniques that will help you improve your diet and reduce stress:

a) Colorful plates: add a variety of colors to your plate by incorporating fruits and vegetables of different hues. Each color represents a unique range of nutrients and antioxidants that promote a healthy mind and body - imagine a rainbow on your plate!

b) Loving hydration: keep your body hydrated with fresh water and tasty herbal teas. Water is essential for optimal functioning of your brain and body. Also, try to reduce consumption of sugary drinks and soft drinks that can negatively affect your mood and energy.

c) Nutritional balance: look for a balanced combination of protein, healthy carbohydrates and healthy fats at each meal. This will help you maintain a stable energy level throughout the day and promote a positive mood and a clear mind.

Practical exercises for adopting healthy eating habits

It's time to put conscious and nutritious eating into practice!

Here are some practical exercises that you can incorporate into your daily life:

a) Food Log: Keep a log of your meals and snacks for a week. This will help you become aware of your food choices and identify patterns that you can adjust to improve your overall well-being.

b) Unhurried meals: take time to enjoy every bite. Avoid eating in a hurry or distracted. Savor the flavors and textures of food. This will help you feel more satisfied and develop a more conscious relationship with food.

c) Smart planning: Set aside time each week to plan your meals and make a healthy shopping list.

Having options available will allow you to make more informed choices and avoid falling into less healthy temptations.

Conscious eating is an act of love towards yourself.

d) Listen to your body: when you feel heavy, tired, swollen or notice that you find it hard to go to the bathroom more than usual, write down what you ate hours before. The body gives us a warning in the form of symptoms so that we know which foods are good for us and which are not, find the balance and choose foods that nourish you both physically and mentally.

Discovering superfoods: mental health boosters

Superfoods have the power to boost our mental health. There is a select group of foods that have been recognized for their exceptional benefits for emotional and cognitive well-being. Don't hesitate to incorporate them into your daily diet to nourish your mind and body optimally.

The Power of Cocoa: Immerse yourself in the delicious and comforting taste of dark chocolate. You'll discover how cocoa, rich in antioxidants and mood-boosting compounds, can elevate your serotonin and endorphin levels, giving you a sense of happiness and well-being.

The wonders of avocado: Learn about the benefits of avocado, a versatile and delicious fruit. You'll discover that its high content of healthy fats, vitamin E and essential nutrients promote brain health and contribute to emotional stability.

The green power of seaweed: dive into the world of seaweed, rich in essential nutrients such as iodine, which is essential for the proper functioning of the thyroid gland and hormonal balance. Discover how these jewels of the sea can bring you a sense of calm and mental clarity.

The brilliance of berries: explore the colorful and juicy universe of berries, such as blackberries, strawberries and blueberries. These little treats are loaded with antioxidants that protect your brain from oxidative stress and improve cognitive function.

The treasure trove of nuts: delve into the world of nuts, such as walnuts, almonds and hazelnuts. You'll discover how these little treasures are packed with omega-3 fatty acids, vitamin E and magnesium, key nutrients to promote mental health and emotional balance.

The splendor of green tea: enjoy a comforting and revitalizing journey through the properties of green tea. You will discover how it's antioxidants and unique compounds, such as L-theanine, can improve your mood, increase concentration and reduce stress.

The fantasy of fermented foods: explores the fascinating dimension of fermented foods, such as sauerkraut, kimchi, kefir and plain yogurt. These foods promote gut health, known as our "second brain," and are linked to mental and emotional health.

By discovering superfoods, we enter a world full of flavors, textures and amazing benefits for our mental health. I invite you to explore and experiment with these foods, incorporating them into your diet in a creative way and enjoying the incredible benefits they bring to your emotional and cognitive well-being.

The importance of hydration: water to nourish body and mind

Now I want to talk to you about something we sometimes overlook, but which is essential for our well-being: hydration. Water is much more than just a refreshing drink, it is a vital element to nourish our body and mind. So sit back, relax and discover how the power of water can transform your life.

We begin by remembering that our body is composed mostly of water. It is the vital liquid that keeps us functioning, helping to transport nutrients, regulate body temperature and eliminate toxins. By drinking enough water, we ensure that we maintain internal balance and optimal health.

Did you know that lack of hydration can affect your cognitive ability? When we don't drink enough water, our brains can experience mental fog, lack of focus and decreased mental clarity. By staying hydrated, we are providing our brain with the fluid it needs to function optimally, which translates into increased focus and mental performance.

Not only does our body benefit from hydration, but so do our emotions. When we are dehydrated, we are more likely to feel irritable, anxious or tired. Drinking plenty of water helps us maintain emotional balance, improving our mood and helping us cope with stress more effectively.

Water is also a beauty elixir! Adequate hydration is essential for radiant, healthy skin. Water helps maintain skin elasticity, prevents dryness and promotes a fresh, youthful appearance. So, if you want to have an enviable complexion, be sure to drink enough water every day.

Now that we know the importance of hydration, how can you incorporate it into your daily life? Here are some practical tips that have really helped me stay well-hydrated:

Always carry a reusable water bottle with you. This way, you will have access to fresh water anytime, anywhere.

Set reminders to drink water periodically throughout the day. You can use mobile apps or simply set alarms on your phone.

Add a touch of flavor to your water with slices of lemon, cucumber or mint. This will make drinking water more enjoyable and refreshing.

Don't wait until you are thirsty! Thirst is a sign of dehydration, so try to drink water before you feel thirsty.

Remember that every time you drink water, you are deeply nourishing your body and mind - don't underestimate the transformative power of hydration!

Keep your water bottle close by and give yourself the gift of conscious and constant hydration - you'll be revitalized and energized, ready to face any challenge life throws at you!

So, here's to a full and well-hydrated life! Cheers!

Probiotic foods: mental and digestive health benefits

Probiotic foods are a source of benefits for our mental and digestive health. Let's start by understanding what probiotics are. These are living microorganisms, such as bacteria and yeasts that, when consumed in adequate amounts, have a positive impact on our health, as they act as little warriors within our digestive system, helping to maintain a healthy balance of beneficial bacteria.

Our digestive system is much more than a food processor. It is linked to our mental and emotional well-being. Probiotics have the ability to improve digestion, helping to break down food and facilitating the absorption of essential nutrients.

Happy digestion allows us to feel light, energetic and free of discomfort.

There is an amazing connection between our gut and our brain, known as the gut-brain axis. Probiotics play a crucial role in this relationship, as they influence the production of neurotransmitters, such as serotonin, which play a key role in our mood and mental well-being. By maintaining a healthy balance of bacteria in the gut, we can experience an improvement in our mood and a reduction in stress and anxiety.

Some delicious options include plain yogurt, kefir, sauerkraut, miso, tempeh and kimchi. These fermented foods contain a host of probiotics that can help you maintain a healthy balance in your gut microbiota.

Did you know that you can also grow your own probiotic foods at home? Home fermentation is a fun and creative way to incorporate probiotic foods into your diet. You can try making your own sauerkraut, kombucha or fermented yogurt. In addition to saving money, you'll be adding a personal touch to your diet and contributing to your mental and digestive well-being.

Remember that every time you enjoy probiotic foods, you are nourishing both your body and your mind. These tiny organisms have a significant impact on our overall health and well-being. So go ahead, embrace the benefits of probiotic foods and feel them fill you with vitality and balance!

We are the protagonists of our own health!

Foods to boost energy and vitality: fighting mental exhaustion

We can harness the power of food to boost our energy and vitality, and combat mental exhaustion. There are a wide variety of delicious and nutritious options that will help us stay energized and full of vitality throughout the day.

The nutrients we consume can impact our energy and vitality, for example: Complex carbohydrates, such as whole grains and legumes, provide us with sustained energy.

Healthy fats, present in foods such as avocados and nuts, guarantee a concentrated source of energy necessary for optimal brain function.

There are also a wide variety of foods that are excellent sources of energy and vitality. From fresh, juicy fruits like oranges and strawberries, to green leafy vegetables like spinach and kale, which are packed with nutrients that keep us energized.

It is important to incorporate lean proteins, such as chicken, fish or tofu, for a feeling of satiety and long-lasting energy. Nor can we leave out of our diet energy-boosting superfoods or revitalizing Superfoods such as chia, full of omega-3 fatty acids and fiber that keep us satiated and full of energy, as well as berries, blueberries and blackberries, which are loaded with antioxidants and vitamins These superfoods are true allies for our mental and physical well-being!

We cannot forget about beverages that help us stay hydrated and energetic throughout the day. Include refreshing options such as coconut water, rich in minerals and electrolytes that replenish energy reserves in your diet. Natural infusions, such as green tea or mate, give us a sustained energy boost and help us keep our herbs focused.

I invite you to experiment and combine these energizing foods in delicious recipes to fill you with vitality and flavor. From smoothies and colorful salads to energy dishes with quality ingredients, you will have endless options to keep your energy and vitality at its peak.

Remember, food is a powerful tool to nourish our body and mind. With a balanced and conscious diet, we can combat mental exhaustion and enjoy a life full of energy and vitality. You deserve to feel vibrant and energetic every day!

Strategies to avoid emotional eating: cultivating a healthy relationship with food.

Often, food can become our emotional refuge, which is why I want to show you how we can free ourselves from that dependence and find a nourishing and satisfying balance.

Before embarking on this journey of change, it is critical to recognize and understand what emotional eating is. Our emotions can influence our eating habits and how we can identify if we are using food as a way to manage our emotions. It is important to learn to listen and understand our internal signals, as this will allow us to make conscious and empowered choices.

Mindful eating will be our great ally in this journey towards a healthy relationship with food. This transformative practice invites us to pay full attention to every bite we eat. By connecting with our senses, savoring each food and cultivating a greater awareness of our nutritional and emotional needs, we will be nourishing, with each bite, our body and mind in a conscious and loving way.

There are healthy alternatives to dealing with our emotions instead of resorting to food, simple but powerful techniques to manage stress, sadness or anxiety in a healthier way. From practicing meditation and mindful breathing to pursuing pleasurable activities and cultivating meaningful relationships, in each of these you will find a variety of tools to nurture your emotions in a positive and satisfying way.

We must learn to recognize our true emotional needs and how to satisfy them without resorting to food. Discovering our passions, our dreams and our goals, connecting with what really makes us feel full and happy, will allow us to maintain a healthy and wholesome relationship with ourselves.

Remember that we are able to free ourselves from emotional eating and cultivate a healthy relationship with food. Through conscious eating, self-knowledge and the search for healthy alternatives, we will be building a path to balance and wholeness.

I encourage you to take the first step towards a loving and nourishing relationship with food!

CHAPTER 11

Weaving support networks: stress-relieving connections

The magic of social support: relieving the burden of stress

Let me share another valuable secret with you: social support can be a healing balm in times of stress. Knowing that you are not alone, that there are people willing to listen and support you, can make all the difference in your mental and emotional well-being.

Meaningful and authentic connections provide us with a safe space where we can share our joys, suspicions and fears, and find comfort and perspective.

Weaving strong connections: techniques for cultivating meaningful relationships

It's time to weave support networks and nurture our social connections!

Here are some practical techniques and exercises that you can apply in your daily life:

a) Active listening: devote time and genuine attention when interacting with others. Listen actively, showing interest and empathy towards their experiences and emotions. This will strengthen the connection and trust in your relationships.

b) Shared moments: Look for opportunities to create memories and shared experiences with your loved ones. Organize group activities, such as outdoor outings, home-cooked dinners or game nights. These moments of connection will strengthen bonds and generate a sense of belonging and mutual support.

c) Practice gratitude: express your appreciation and gratitude to those who have been supportive. Whether it's through a thank you note, a caring text message or simply saying "thank you," showing your gratitude will strengthen bonds and foster a culture of support in your relationships.

d) Calls for no reason: don't wait until you have something to say to call. Remember how, years ago, we would call our friends to talk about anything, to ask them how it went with that person they met or if they played the new video game they bought. Just call and ask, "how are you?" That will create a very nice feeling in the person you are calling, since it is not a call to ask for a favor or to be heard, but quite the opposite. This is a nice way to show affection to the people we love.

Meaningful connections not only provide us with emotional support, but also give us a sense of purpose and meaning in life. Striving to cultivate authentic and nurturing relationships is a gift both to ourselves and to those around us.

The importance of authentic communication: building bridges of connection

In our search for inner serenity and balance, we cannot underestimate the power of genuine and meaningful communication in our relationships.

When I talk about authentic communication, I mean expressing ourselves from the deepest part of our being, without fear of being judged or rejected. It is a courageous and liberating act that allows us to build stronger and more authentic connections with others.

Authentic communication is a powerful tool for building bridges of connection with others. It allows us to express our deepest selves, listen with empathy and build more authentic and meaningful relationships. As we cultivate authentic communication, we find a space where we feel understood, valued and fundamentally supported.

First, it is important to remember that authentic communication begins with ourselves. Before we can convey our emotions and thoughts clearly and sincerely, we need to be in tune with our own emotions and accept them without judgment. Allow yourself to feel what you feel and validate your own inner experiences.

Once we are in touch with our emotions, we can share our truth with others. This involves expressing our thoughts, desires and needs in an open and respectful manner. It is important to remember that authentic communication does not mean imposing our opinion on others, but rather seeking mutual understanding and building bridges of connection.

Authentic communication also requires empathetic listening. When we open ourselves to genuinely listen to others, we create a safe space where they feel valued and understood. Pay active attention to what they are telling you, show interest and avoid distractions. Allow them to express themselves without interruption and avoid judging or criticizing their words. Remember that empathy brings us together and strengthens our relationships.

In addition, it is essential to be aware of our nonverbal language. Our gestures, facial expressions and tone of voice can convey more than the words themselves. Keep your body language open and receptive, and use a friendly, calm tone to convey your message. Remember that effective communication is not only about the words we say, but also how we say them.

I invite you to practice authentic communication in your daily relationships. Cultivate a space of trust where you can share your thoughts and emotions without fear, and give that space to others as well.

Circles of support: finding your community in times of stress

In times of stress, it's normal to feel overwhelmed and exhausted. But don't forget that you don't have to carry all the weight by yourself. Seeking support from others can be a source of relief, strength and motivation. Finding a community is like finding a refuge in the midst of the storm, a place where we can share our concerns, find solace and gain new perspectives.

The first key to forming circles of support is to open ourselves to the possibility of connecting with others. Sometimes, in our eagerness to be independent, we can forget that we all need a shoulder to lean on. Accept that asking for help is not a sign of weakness, but a sign of courage and wisdom. Allow yourself to receive the support and love you deserve.

Once we are open to the community, it is important to seek out people with similar interests and values to our own. Whether you find your tribe in local support groups, or online through activities you enjoy, the key is to share spaces with people who understand your challenges and provide a safe and supportive environment. We all deserve to feel understood and accepted by those around us.

In addition, it is critical to remember that building a strong community is a gradual process. Don't expect to find a circle of support overnight. Building meaningful relationships takes time, patience and dedication. Participate in group activities, interact with others in a genuine way, and keep an open mind to build lasting connections.

Within circles of support, it is important to cultivate an atmosphere of empathy and compassion. Actively listen to others, provide emotional support and celebrate each member's accomplishments. We are all on the same path to inner serenity and balance and can learn from each other. Together, we form a network of support where we encourage each other and remind each other that we are not alone.

Finding your community and forming circles of support is essential to dealing with stress in a healthy way. Don't be afraid to ask for help and open yourself to the possibility of meaningful connections. Surrounding ourselves with people with similar interests or problems to our own strengthens us and helps us find the serenity and balance we seek.

Find your community, share your concerns and celebrate your triumphs with people who understand and support you.

Online resources: discovering virtual support communities

In our search for inner serenity and balance, we often encounter challenges and need to connect with others who understand our experiences. As we move forward, technology allows us to discover online communities where we can find support, inspiration and helpful resources.

Virtual support communities are online spaces where people with similar interests and challenges come together to share experiences, support each other and learn together. These communities offer a digital refuge where we can find empathy, understanding and practical advice for dealing with the challenges we face in our quest for serenity.

The first advantage of online communities is their accessibility. Through online platforms and social networks, we can connect with people from all over the world, overcoming geographical barriers and finding a global community. No matter where you are physically located, you can always find a virtual place to belong and receive the support you need.

In addition, virtual support communities offer us a variety of valuable resources. In these spaces, we can find articles, videos, podcasts and other materials to help us better understand our challenges and discover new strategies for cultivating inner serenity. We can also participate in group discussions, ask questions and share our own perspectives and experiences.

One of the main strengths of online communities is the diversity of voices and experiences found within them. By joining an online community, you will have the opportunity to interact with people of different backgrounds, ages and perspectives. This enriches our learning process and allows us to expand our view of the world. Together, we can be nurtured and inspired by each other's success stories.

When immersing yourself in a virtual community, it is important to remember that each person is unique and has his or her own journey. Appreciate differences and show respect for others, even when you disagree. Be open and willing to learn from others, making the most of the opportunities for personal growth and connection that these communities offer.

I encourage you to be active within the online communities. Share your experiences, doubts and achievements with others. Don't be afraid to ask for help and offer your support to those who need it. Remember that the true power of these communities lies in the interaction and collaboration among their members.

The healing power of pets

When I arrive home after a long day and open the door to my home, the first thing I see is my faithful furry companions, Drako and Sabry, both of whom are always in the driveway waiting for me with their infectious joy. As I stroke their soft fur, I almost immediately feel the stress and worries melt away.

This doesn't just happen to me, as pets are special beings that provide us with companionship, unconditional love and a deep connection that can be healing to our body, mind and spirit and have a special gift to bring us comfort and ease our anxiety. Just being near them fills us with a sense of calm and well-being.

Scientific research backs up what many of us already know in our hearts: pets have the power to improve our physical and emotional health. Studies have shown that interacting with animals can lower blood pressure, lower heart rate and release endorphins, the happy hormones, in our bodies. In addition, the presence of a pet can decrease feelings of loneliness and increase feelings of social connection.

One of the ways pets help us heal is through their ability to give us unconditional love. They accept us as we are, without judgment, and teach us the importance of loyalty and compassion. When we put our pets or play with them, we experience a deep connection that fills us with joy and makes us feel loved. This pure, selfless love is a balm for our souls and reminds us how important it is to give and receive affection.

In addition, pets motivate us to be more active, healthy and maintain a routine. Walking our dog gives us the opportunity to enjoy the outdoors, exercise and connect with nature. Playing with our pets, whether throwing a ball or playing with an interactive toy, helps us release tension and provides moments of fun and joy.

If you are considering adding a pet to your life, it is important to take into account your circumstances and responsibilities. Each species and breed has its own needs and requirements, so be sure to do your research and choose the pet that best suits your lifestyle. It is also essential to provide them with proper care, including a balanced diet, regular veterinary care and lots of love and affection.

If you already have a pet, I encourage you to make the most of its presence in your life. Take the time to enjoy its company, play with it and give it the care it needs. Let them be your ally in times of stress and sadness, and celebrate the joy they bring to your home.

CHAPTER 12

Integration. a tailor-made path: your personalized plan for stress reduction

The importance of a tailored plan: shaping your wellbeing

I am excited to share with you practical tools and inspirational tips that will help you take the necessary steps towards a more balanced and calmer life.

Designing a personalized plan is key to effectively combating stress. By creating a tailored approach, you have the opportunity to identify the techniques and practices that best suit you and your lifestyle.

There is no one-size-fits-all plan when it comes to stress reduction. Your personalized plan will give you the freedom to explore and select the tools that resonate with you.

Weaving techniques together: integrating the best of each world

Now it is time to bring together all the techniques we have explored throughout this book.

Combine the strategies that have given you positive results and experiment with new ideas to see what works best for you.

For example, you could integrate *mindfulness* practice with physical exercise and the use of positive affirmations.

The key is to find a combination that empowers you and helps you deal with stress in a holistic way.

Your personal action plan: practical steps to reduce stress

It's time to create your own stress reduction plan. Here are some practical exercises to help you take the first steps:

a) Self-evaluation: reflection on the techniques and strategies that resonated with you during this journey. Consider your personal preferences, interests and goals. This will help you select the most appropriate tools for your personalized plan.

b) Set goals: define clear and achievable goals that allow you to measure your progress. These goals may be related to the practice of specific techniques, the incorporation of healthy habits or the reduction of stressors in your life.

c) Action plan: Create a detailed action plan that includes the specific steps you will take to implement your customized plan. Set a realistic timeline and track your progress over time.

Remember that this plan is flexible and evolving. As you grow and face new challenges, you can adjust and adapt it to meet your changing needs.

Congratulations on completing this transformative journey!

I hope you have found inspiration and valuable tools to deal with stress in your life.

Please keep in mind that change takes time and effort, but with perseverance and self-compassion, you can achieve a more balanced and fulfilling life.

I wish you all the best on your path to good!

CHAPTER 13

Embracing balance: powerful tools for stress management

Uncovering the behaviors that fuel stress

We are almost to the last chapter of our journey towards a calmer and more balanced life.

I am excited to share with you these inspiring and accessible tools that will help you find calm in the midst of life's storms.

In this chapter, we will explore a variety of tips, techniques and definitive strategies to efficiently manage stress.

It is important that we identify the behaviors that perpetuate stress in our lives. Let's take a moment to reflect on our daily routines and our reactions to stressful situations.

Are there repeating patterns that plunge us into a constant cycle of stress? By becoming aware of these behaviors, we can begin to challenge them and replace them with healthier, more balanced actions.

Visualization: creating your oasis of peace

Visualization is a powerful technique that will allow us to imagine calm and relaxing scenarios, which will help us to calm our minds and body.

Close your eyes and imagine a serene place where you feel safe and at peace. It can be a beach, a lush garden or any environment that gives you a sense of tranquility.

Visualize yourself there, breathing deeply and letting tensions dissolve.

This practice will help you find moments of calm even in the midst of chaos.

The magic of music: tuning in to your wellbeing

Music has an incredible power to affect our mood and reduce stress.

Find melodies that convey peace and joy, and create a special playlist for moments of relaxation.

Whether you prefer soft and relaxing music, or energetic rhythms that make you move, let the music envelop you and transport you to a state of serenity.

Activities backed by science: the power of the tried and tested

There are numerous activities supported by scientific studies that help reduce stress effectively.

Some of these include the practice of *mindfulness* meditation, yoga, deep breathing and regular physical exercise.

These activities not only lower stress levels but also promote overall mental and physical health. Find the one that resonates with you and make space to incorporate it into your daily life.

Final tips for a more balanced life

To close this journey together, here are some tips and recommendations that you can apply in your daily life to keep stress at bay:

Set healthy boundaries: learn to say "no" when necessary and prioritize your emotional well-being.

Practice gratitude: Take a few minutes each day to be thankful for the positive things in your life. This will help you cultivate a positive mindset and appreciate what you have.

Seek support: Don't be afraid to ask for help when you need it. Connect with friends, family or mental health professionals who can provide support and guidance.

Take care of yourself: Make regular time for activities that bring you joy and relaxation. Whether it's reading a book, enjoying a hot bath or practicing your favorite hobby, give yourself permission to take care of yourself.

CHAPTER 14

Shining in your own light: the transforming conclusion

Congratulations! We have reached the end of this journey of self-discovery and personal growth.

In this last chapter, I want to share with you some final thoughts and provide you with additional tools to keep you shining in your own light.

It has been an honor to accompany you on this journey, and I hope you feel inspired and empowered to embrace a life full of joy, peace and authenticity.

Celebrating your progress

Before moving on, take a moment to recognize and celebrate all the progress you have made so far.

Every step you have taken towards a more balanced and stress-free life is an important achievement.

Allow yourself to feel gratitude for the road you have traveled and for the dedication you have shown in your quest for wellness.

Nurturing your inner self

Self-care is an essential aspect of a balanced life. Be sure to set aside time and space to nurture your inner self.

This may include practices such as meditation, journaling, practicing gratitude, or spending time in creative activities that will bring you joy.
Listen to the needs of your heart and commit to honor them.

Expanding your support network

Remember that you are not alone on this journey. Look for opportunities to connect with others who share your values and aspirations.
Participate in support groups, online communities or social activities that allow you to make meaningful connections.
By sharing your experiences and listening to those of others, you will find strength and mutual enrichment.

Daily reminders of your inner power

In your daily life, it is important to keep the awareness of your inner power alive. Find reminders that inspire you and remind you of your ability to overcome challenges and live a fulfilling life.
You can place inspirational quotes in visible places, carry a symbolic object with you or even create a list of positive affirmations that boost your confidence and self-esteem.

Following your own path

Always remember that this is your personal journey. Don't compare yourself to others or feel pressured to meet external expectations. Each person has his or her own pace and needs.

Listen to your intuition and follow the path that resonates with your most authentic self. Trust yourself and be true to who you are every step of the way.

The beginning of a new adventure

This is not the end but the beginning of a new adventure. Continue to explore, learn and grow on your path to wellness and wholeness. Allow yourself to continue discovering new tools, strategies and approaches to help you maintain balance and harmony in your life.

Thank you for allowing me to be a part of your journey to a more peaceful and fulfilling life!

I encourage you to continue to apply the teachings shared in this book and adapt them to your own experience. Remember, you are the protagonist of your story and you have the power to create the life you desire.

I wish you all the best in this new chapter of your life - go ahead, shine in your own light and live with passion!

Conclusion

A new beginning for a full and balanced life

Throughout this ebook, we have explored valuable tools and strategies for managing stress and cultivating our mental and emotional well-being.

Now is the time to take a step forward and start applying everything you have learned in your daily life.

During this process, we have discovered that self-care is fundamental to our overall well-being. From setting healthy boundaries to practicing gratitude and self-reflection, every small action you take in the direction of self-care will make a big difference in your life.

You are not alone in this journey. There is a support network around you, made up of friends, family and communities that are willing to lend their support and understanding. Take advantage of these connections, share your experiences and learn from others. Together, we can grow and overcome any challenge that comes our way.

Allow yourself to explore various techniques and find those that work best for you. Meditation, conscious breathing, physical exercise, eating well, writing, or practicing creative activities are just some of the tools available to you.

Experiment and discover which practices help you find calm, clarity and well-being in your daily life.

Balance is an ongoing process. Life is full of ups and downs, and it is natural to face challenges and stressful moments. Don't be discouraged if you encounter obstacles along the way.

Allow yourself to learn from each experience and remember that each new day is an opportunity to begin anew and cultivate a fuller, more satisfying life.

I am honored to have been a part of your journey. I want you to know that you have within you the strength and ability to face any adversity and create the life you desire.

Trust yourself, listen to your intuition and stay focused on your deepest goals and values.

Real change happens through action. So I encourage you to take one small step towards change once you finish reading these words.

It can be as simple as taking a deep breath, writing in your gratitude journal or committing to setting healthier boundaries in your life.

This is just the beginning of your journey to a fuller and more balanced life. Keep exploring, learning and growing. I am excited for you and the future that awaits you.

Thank you for allowing me to be part of this amazing journey with you!

Together, we can create a life full of purpose, joy and well-being.

BONUS

Bonus 1

Affirmations for self-transformation

Affirmations are positive statements that help you to reprogram your mind and foster positive change in rour life. In the context of the Enneagram, we can use specific affirmations based on each personality type to promote self-transformation and personal growth.

Below, let's look at which affirmations are effective in helping each personality type on a day-to-day basis:

Type 1 - The Perfectionist Personality

I am enough just the way I am. I allow myself to make mistakes and learn from them.

I recognize that progress is more important than perfection. I allow myself to grow and evolve rather than seek absolute excellence.

I appreciate my accomplishments and recognize that success is not determined solely by the end results, but by the effort and dedication I put into each task.

Type 2 - The Helper

I value my own well-being and set healthy boundaries. I allow myself to be supported and cared for.

I learn to say "no" when necessary and set healthy boundaries to maintain my emotional and physical well-being.

I recognize that taking care of myself enables me to be better able to help others more effectively and sustainably.

Type 3 - The Achiever Personality

My value is not dependent on my external accomplishments. My authenticity is my greatest strength.

My worth is not tied solely to my external accomplishments, but to my authenticity and the quality of my personal relationships. I appreciate moments of rest and enjoyment, recognizing that true happiness does not depend solely on achieving goals, but on enjoying the journey.

Type 4 - The Individualist

I celebrate my uniqueness and accept myself in all my facets. My creativity lights my path. I explore and embrace my inner diversity. Every part of me has its purpose and contributes to my uniqueness and personal growth. I appreciate the power of my creativity and allow it to guide my choices, bringing new perspectives and opportunities into my life.

Type 5 - The Investigator

I trust my inner wisdom and share my knowledge with others. I am part of the whole. I trust my intuition and inner wisdom when making decisions and seeking knowledge. My unique perspective enriches my environment and benefits others.

I generously share my knowledge and experiences, knowing that in doing so, I contribute to the growth and development of those around me.

Type 6 - The Loyalist

I trust myself and the process of life. I am courageous and able to face any challenge. I trust myself and my ability to face challenges. I am constantly growing and developing and have the courage to overcome any obstacle that comes my way.

I cultivate relationships based on loyalty and mutual trust, creating a supportive and collaborative environment in my life.

Type 7 - The Enthusiast

I find fulfillment in the present and appreciate the blessings of each moment. Joy is within me. I find joy and fulfillment in each present moment, appreciating the little things that bring me happiness and gratitude.

I cultivate a mindset of abundance and optimism, recognizing that joy and happiness are inner states that I can nurture and experience at any moment.

Type 8 - The Protector Personality

I am strong and powerful, allowing myself to be vulnerable and show compassion toward others. I recognize my personal strength and power, and also allow myself to show vulnerability and

compassion   to   others.
I use my strength and protection to care for and support those I care about, creating a safe and loving   environment   around   me.

Type 9 - The Peacemaker Personality

I assert myself and express my needs clearly and assertively. My voice is important and valued.
I assert and express my needs and desires clearly and respectfully, knowing that my voice and opinions   are   important   and   valued.
I seek harmony and peaceful conflict resolution, creating a space where everyone feels heard and understood.
For   good   use   of   these   and   other   positive affirmations, it is advisable to:
Be aware of your thoughts: Observe your thoughts and detect negative or limiting patterns. Identify the beliefs you want to change and replace them with positive affirmations.
Choose powerful affirmations: Create affirmations that resonate with you and are relevant to your personal growth. They should be positive, in the present   tense   and   in   the   first   person.
Repeat and reinforce: Repeat your affirmations daily, preferably in moments of peace, when waking up   or   before   going   to   sleep.   Reinforce   their effectiveness by visualizing yourself living the reality you desire while reciting them.

Reinforce your affirmations with consistent actions: Affirmations are most effective when they are accompanied by consistent actions. Align your actions and behaviors with the beliefs and attitudes you wish to manifest in your life.

By using affirmations based on each Enneagram personality type, you can direct your focus to the specific aspects you wish to strengthen and transform in your life.

Remember that affirmations are not a magic bullet, but a tool to help you reprogram your mind and create positive change in your life.

Using effective affirmations requires commitment and consistent practice. As you practice and commit to affirmations, you will gradually begin to cultivate a more positive, confident and empowered mindset.

Change takes time and effort. Be patient with yourself and maintain an attitude of openness and receptivity. Don't expect instant results, but practice consistently and trust the process.

By adopting positive and realistic affirmations, you can reprogram your mind and begin to align your thoughts, beliefs and actions with your true potential.

Don't be discouraged if at first you don't feel an immediate change, consistent practice and perseverance are key to lasting results. Over time, affirmations can help you change your negative thought patterns, strengthen your self-confidence and enable you to achieve your goals and aspirations.

Tailor affirmations to your own language and way of thinking. Choose words and phrases that create a sense of connection and empowerment, affirmations should be realistic and believable to you, as your mind needs to accept them as true for them to be effective.

As you practice affirmations consistently and integrate them into your daily life, you will begin to notice positive changes in the way you think, feel and act. For example, if you affirm that you are a healthy person, support that affirmation with healthy food choices and regular exercise. Powerful affirmations can be an invaluable tool for self-transformation and personal growth. By combining effective affirmations with clear visualizations and consistent actions, you can cultivate a positive mindset and build a life more aligned with your true self.

Bonus 2
Cultivating Emotional Resilience

Emotional resilience is an essential skill for facing life's challenges and adversities with strength and adaptability. It allows us to bounce back from difficulties and maintain a positive attitude. Emotional resilience is essential to our emotional and mental well-being, helping us to cope with stressful situations, overcome failures and maintain a positive mindset. By cultivating it, we develop the ability to manage our emotions in a healthy way and build a solid foundation for personal growth. There are several aspects of our personality that emotional resilience can strengthen. For example: Adaptation to change: it allows us to adapt to life's changes and transitions more effectively. It helps us to accept and overcome obstacles, finding new opportunities in the midst of adversity. Stress management: Helps us to manage stress more efficiently. It allows us to identify our emotional responses to stressful situations and take measures to reduce the negative impact of stress on our health and well-being.
Self-confidence: Strengthens our self-confidence. It helps us believe in our abilities to overcome challenges and gives us the courage to face difficult situations.

There are several practices that can help you strengthen your emotional resilience. Here are some recommended exercises and techniques: Emotional self-awareness: take time to explore and understand your own emotions. Practice mindfulness and introspection to recognize your emotional patterns and how they affect you. This will allow you to develop a greater awareness of yourself and your emotional responses. Building a support network: Cultivate strong, supportive relationships with family, friends and members of your community. Share your feelings and experiences with people you trust, as this can provide you with the emotional support you need during difficult times.

Seek social support: Seek support from people close to you, such as friends, family or support groups. Sharing your experiences and emotions with others can help you gain different perspectives and feel understood. Participate in social activities that provide positive connections and allow you to feel part of a community.

Practice self-compassion: Learn to treat yourself with kindness and understanding when you face challenges or make mistakes. Recognize that we all make mistakes and that personal growth involves learning from them. Instead of judging yourself harshly, practice self-compassion and give yourself permission to be human.

Maintain a learning attitude: Cultivate a mindset that is open and receptive to continuous learning. Consider every experience as an opportunity to grow and learn more about yourself. Be curious and willing to explore new perspectives and approaches to life.

Acceptance and adaptation: Learn to accept circumstances that you cannot change and focus on adapting to them. Recognize that change is an inevitable part of life and look for new ways to approach challenges.

Practice problem solving: Develop effective problem solving skills. Break challenges into smaller, more manageable steps and look for creative solutions. This will help you face obstacles with a proactive mindset.

Self-care: Prioritize your physical and mental well-being. Spending time on activities that bring you joy, rest and rejuvenation is critical to cultivating emotional resilience. Set healthy boundaries in your life and learn to say "no" when necessary. Self-care also involves maintaining a balanced diet, getting enough rest and maintaining a proper sleep routine.

Develop coping skills: Learn healthy coping techniques to manage stress and negative emotions. This may include regular physical exercise, relaxation techniques such as meditation or deep breathing, and pursuing activities that help you express your emotions, such as writing in a journal or practicing a hobby.

Cultivating positive thoughts: Practice gratitude and focusing on positive aspects of your life. Challenge your negative thoughts and replace them with positive affirmations. Make a list of past accomplishments and personal strengths to remind yourself of your ability to overcome obstacles and face challenges.

Developing emotional resilience is an ongoing process that requires practice and dedication. By strengthening our ability to manage emotions and adapt to difficult situations, we can face life's challenges with confidence and maintain a positive outlook.

Use these exercises and techniques to build a solid foundation for your emotional well-being and personal growth.

Remember to be kind to yourself during this journey of self-transformation.

Bonus 3
Building Healthy Relationships

Healthy and meaningful relationships are fundamental to our emotional and personal well-being. They provide us with support, companionship and a sense of deep connection. However, building healthy relationships can be challenging, as each individual brings unique experiences and patterns of behavior.

The foundation of any healthy relationship is open and honest communication, this involves: Learning to express our feelings, thoughts and needs clearly and respectfully.

- Actively listening to your partner, friend or family member, showing genuine interest and empathy.
  Setting clear boundaries in relationships, this is essential to ensure mutual respect and emotional balance.
- Learning to say "no" when necessary and to set boundaries in uncomfortable situations.
- Trust is a fundamental pillar in healthy relationships. To build it, it is important to: Being authentic.
- Follow through on promises and commitments.

Avoid manipulation, dishonesty and deception.

- Practicing empathy and understanding by putting yourself in the other person's shoes and validating their emotions and perspectives.
- Identifying and addressing toxic patterns, abusive behaviors or disrespect in relationships.
- Overcoming toxic patterns requires personal work and mutual commitment. You can seek professional support or consider therapy to work on healing and change.

It is important to remember that each relationship is unique and requires constant attention. By developing greater awareness of yourself and your relationship patterns, you will be able to nurture and strengthen your connections with others. Remember that healthy relationships also involve taking care of yourself. Set boundaries and make time for physical and mental self-care. By building healthy relationships, you will be cultivating an environment of support, trust and mutual growth. Through mindfulness and commitment, you can create lasting, meaningful relationships that propel you toward a fuller, more satisfying life.

Bonus 4

Visualization and personal transformation

Visualization can be an effective way to explore and deepen your inner self. It is a powerful tool that allows us to access our imagination and create vivid and meaningful mental images.

Through visualization, we can connect with our deepest goals, dreams and desires and use this powerful tool to enhance our self-awareness and personal growth.

In this bonus, we will learn some visualization exercises that will help us transform our lives in a positive and meaningful way.

Let's look at some visualization exercises that can help us boost our self-knowledge:

The Hall of Mirrors: Imagine you walk into a room full of mirrors. Each one reflects a different facet of your personality, your strengths, your weaknesses, your dreams and your fears. Look closely at each reflection and reflect on what it reveals about you. Use this visualization to gain a deeper understanding of who you are.

The Inner Garden: Close your eyes and imagine that you are walking through a beautiful garden. Each element of the garden represents an aspect of your life: the flowers symbolize your relationships, the trees represent your personal growth, the water reflects your inner tranquility. Notice how each element looks and how they interact with each other. Reflect on what you would like to change, improve or cultivate in your inner garden. Use this visualization to explore your desires and goals in different areas of your life. Our imagination has a powerful impact on our perception and our ability to create positive changes in our lives. Let's use imagination as a tool for positive change.

Journey into the future: Close your eyes and imagine that you are in a distant future, where you have achieved all your goals and feel fully realized. Observe your life in this future and visualize all the details: how you feel, what you have achieved, how you relate to others, etc. Use this visualization to connect with your vision of success and to set clear and motivating goals in the present. Transformation of limiting beliefs: Identify a belief that is holding you back from moving toward your goals. Close your eyes and imagine holding that belief in your hands. Visualize transforming that belief into something positive and empowering. Imagine the belief becoming a seed that you plant in the fertile soil of your mind, and enjoy how it grows into a new belief that strengthens you and propels you toward success.

Remember that visualization is a personal practice unique to each person. You can adapt the visualization exercises to your own needs and preferences. Find a quiet place, close your eyes, breathe deeply and immerse yourself in the imaginative experience.

By using these powerful visualizations, you will develop a deeper connection with yourself, discovering new possibilities and potential in your life.

Visualization not only helps you focus on your goals and dreams, but also provides you with an effective tool for overcoming obstacles, strengthening your confidence and awakening your creativity. As you immerse yourself in your imagination, you open yourself to new perspectives and possibilities, creating a solid foundation for growth and positive change in your life. In this way, you can move toward manifesting your true self and living a full and meaningful life.

Visualizations are a valuable tool for personal transformation, allowing you to enhance your self-knowledge, explore your desires and goals, and transform limiting beliefs into empowering ones

GOOD WILL

Helping others without expectation of anything in return has been proven to lead to increased happiness and satisfaction in life.

I would love to give you the chance to experience that same feeling during your reading or listening experience today...

All it takes is a few moments of your time to answer one simple question:

Would you make a difference in the life of someone you've never met—without spending any money or seeking recognition for your good will?

If so, I have a small request for you.

If you've found value in your reading experience today, I humbly ask that you take a brief moment right now to leave an honest review of this book. It won't cost you anything but 30 seconds of your time—just a few seconds to share your thoughts with others.

Your voice can go a long way in helping someone else find the same inspiration and knowledge that you have.

Are you familiar with leaving a review for a Kindle, or e-reader book? If so, it's simple:

If you're reading on Kindle or an e-reader, simply scroll to the last page of the book and swipe up—the review should prompt from there.

If you're on a Paperback or any other physical format of this book, you can find the book page on Amazon (or wherever you bought this) and leave your review right there.

Greetings,
Simone Keys

Made in the USA
Middletown, DE
30 July 2023

35986950R00086